THE BIG BOOK o' AWESOME ACTIVITIES

Kidsbooks®

Visit us at www.kidsbooks.com®

Search & Finds®,
Mazes, Crosswords,
Word Searches,
and More!

Get ready to for hours of brain teasing
fun while you sharpen your observation and
concentration skills with
The Big Book of
Awesome Activities!

If you get stumped on any of the puzzles,
don't worry—we put the answers
in the back of the book!

The entire family will enjoy this activity
book anytime and anywhere so start
teasing your brain and see if we
challenged you enough!

Kidsbooks®

What Doesn't Belong?

Circle the one thing in each group that doesn't belong.

Group 1

DIRT
SEEDS
FLOWERS
BUS
SHOVEL

Group 2

CLOWN
JUGGLER
BASKETBALL
ELEPHANT
ACROBAT

Group 3

BALL
BAT
GLOVE
UNIFORM
FISH

Group 4

WATER
JUICE
HOT DOG
MILK
TEA

Answer on page 232

At the Movies

Use the clues below to complete this crossword puzzle.

ACROSS
2 Singing
8 Serious
10 Facing danger
11 Terrorize the audience.

DOWN
1 Real life stuff
2 Scary creature
3 No talking!
4 Lots of laughs
5 Cartoons
6 Magical realms
7 Aboard starships
9 Keep 'em moving.

5

Decode-a-Message

Use the code key below to find a message that has to do with pets.

A=5   G=8   K=16   O=14   T=7
C=10   H=4   L=9   R=1   U=2
D=3   I=12   N=6   S=11   W=13
E=17   Y=15

__ __ __   __ __ __ __'
15 14 2   10 5 6 7

__ __ __ __ __   __ __   __ __ __
7 17 5 10 4   5 6   14 9 3

__ __ __   __ __ __
3 14 8   6 17 13

__ __ __ __ __ __.
7 1 12 10 16 11

6

Answer on page 232

Double Dogs

Can you find the two pictures that are exactly alike?

Answer on page 232

Unbelievable

Can you make **25** words or more from this word?

UNBELIEVABLE

Strawberry Picking

Follow the path from **Start** to **Finish** to help the
boy get to the end of the strawberry field.

9

Fun at the Park

Use the pictures below to complete this crossword puzzle.

Answer on page 233

Carry Away

Solve this rebus puzzle to find something that would be used to carry things.

Harbor Hunt

Find **three sets of two objects** that rhyme with each other.

Answer on page 234

A night at the Movies

Search, find, and circle these **10** things.

FAIRY
TIRE
FISHING ROD

WATERMELON
GORILLA
STRAWBERRY
VIOLIN

SCISSORS
SNOW GLOBE
RHINOCEROS

13

Fun at the Fair

Find 10 differences between the picture on the top and the one on the bottom.

Answer on page 234

Word Scramble

Unscramble each of these words, using the clues.

UKPHNCIM
(Small, cute mammal)

_ _ _ _ _ _ _ _

NATRAMETP
(Place to live)

_ _ _ _ _ _ _ _ _

RAPSIEADP
(Vanish)

_ _ _ _ _ _ _ _ _

MICRANLI
(Someone who breaks the law)

_ _ _ _ _ _ _ _

PUSTCES
(Imagine, guess)

_ _ _ _ _ _ _

LCEIVHE
(Car, boat, train)

_ _ _ _ _ _ _

IPRGONPD
(Falling)

_ _ _ _ _ _ _ _

RNSODRUU
(Encase, enclose)

_ _ _ _ _ _ _ _

National Parks

Find these National Parks in this word search.
Look up, down, backward, forward, and diagonally.

Yosemite   Glacier
Yellowstone   Redwood
Acadia   Sequoia
Olympic   Saguaro
Everglades   Shenandoah

```
O G X J V G K O D J I U N Z Q D L E K S
R I L N Q Y S W X P A U O O T H P P L R
G K I D G O E U S L K I B V C G Z O K K
I K S V D S U V U A K V A B K H D N B O
E R W X K E I J E J G I M N H V Y V X J
S N T H P M D W P R O U O L Y M P I C H
P B O R C I T Y K U G B A V C M K Z E A
S M K T V T R Q Q R Z L C R W H K J B O
U A R D S E L E D V Q H A R O K Q G F D
N J W M L W S O G L X Z S D L N R K R N
R V Q X A T O X S B X I U K E U R H K A
O N X W F W O L R T N X Y Y H S L G O N
X G A L D I B I L Z W L T R Z S P C K E
A S T E O W L F E E C A E T C Q V T G H
A I R O U K X Z D T Y I B E W P O I V S
M I S H I R D U R H C B Y Z C H Y O C U
G D D G S V X U A A L B I R C H I D J K
T W E A C Q I L L D X R G R E P P O D J
D X Y R C P D G V J S Y N J Q T G J X H
Y B U L G A T K F S H X R A D E C N D E
```

16

Unsramble and Fill-In

Unscramble the words below and use them
to fill in the sentences.

T A E R B T _____

R M R E M D U _____

F S R E R U _____

R E A G N D _____

I S T I P R _____

When starting a _____ , you need lots of rich soil.

The _____ hit a long home run to deep right field.

The _____ got very excited seeing the enormous waves in the ocean.

The ghost hunter captured evidence of a _____ with her electronic equipment.

The _____ in the band played a long, loud solo.

Answer on page 235

Communicating

Use the clues below to complete this crossword puzzle.

ACROSS

3 Typing with your thumbs
4 Put this in a mailbox.
6 Call me up.
8 Through the machine, over the wires
10 A chat

DOWN

1 Dots and dashes
2 Call from anywhere.
5 Watch your favorite TV show.
7 Tune it in and listen.
9 Computer message

Decode-a-Riddle

Use the code key below to decode and solve this riddle.

!= A	* = H	> = O	? = V
@ = B	(= I	[= P	/ = W
# = C	+ = J	] = Q	\ = X
$ = D	) = K	" = R	} = Y
% = E	; = L	" = S	{ = Z
^ = F	: = M	' = T	
& = G	< = N	' = U	

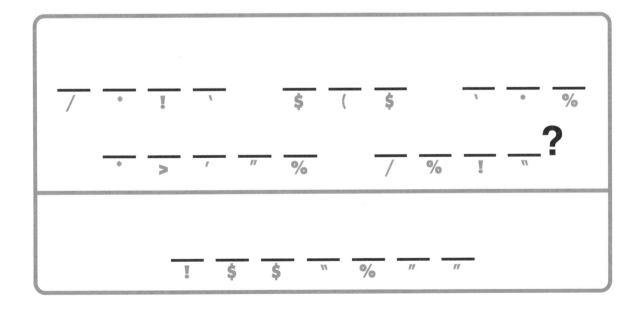

_ _ _ _   _ _ _   _ _ _
/ * ! `    $ ( $    ` * %

_ _ _ _ _   _ _ _ _ ?
* > ' " %   / % ! "

_ _ _ _ _ _ _
! $ $ " % " "

Word Game

Look at the words in the box below. Figure out a common phrase that uses these two words and has to do with love.

HEAD
HEALS

_ _ _ _   _ _ _ _ _

_ _ _ _ _ _

Answer on page 236

Beautiful

Can you make **25** words or more from this word?

_____   _____

_____   _____

_____   _____

_____   _____

_____   _____

_____   _____

_____   _____

_____   _____

_____   _____

_____   _____

_____   _____

Circus Maze

Follow the path from **Start** to **Finish** to get from
the lion stand to the center of the maze.

Extreme Sports

Use the pictures below to complete this crossword puzzle.

ACROSS

1

2

3

DOWN

1   4

23

All Mixed Up

First, figure out what the rebus icons are below.
Then, combine the rebuses to figure out what the answer is.

House Call

Find **three sets of two objects** that rhyme with each other.

Snowball Fight

Search, find, and circle these **10** things.

~~ALIEN~~
~~WHALE~~
~~BEACH BALL~~

~~GLOBE~~
~~MUFFIN~~
CLOCK
BIRTHDAY CAKE

SPOON
WRENCH
GREEN CLOVER

The Big Apple

Find 10 differences between the picture on the top and the one on the bottom.

Answer on page 237

Word Scramble

Unscramble each of these words, using the clues.

IRLAONIG
(Unique)

_ _ _ _ _ _ _ _

KCEJTA
(Coat)

_ _ _ _ _ _

RUTENA
(The great outdoors)

_ _ _ _ _ _

TARPREN
(Teammate)

_ _ _ _ _ _ _

RAFORDW
(Moving ahead)

_ _ _ _ _ _ _

NOEBLG
(Connected to)

_ _ _ _ _ _

SBENRUM
(Count with these)

_ _ _ _ _ _ _

ANEOSS
(Time of year)

_ _ _ _ _ _

28

Backyard Games

Find these backyard games in the word search.
Look up, down, backward, forward, and diagonally.

Hide and seek   Baseball
Kickball   Football
Volleyball   Badminton
Bocce   Horseshoes
Tag   Croquet

S E O H S E S R O H T H O I
W P O E F G W L L E X C V I
J C B K C O K E U Q O S S K
S L L E G C O Q O G C D A A
I T L E K H O T R A V R A I
T A A S C R B F B T P N Y L
G O B D C K B J E A O S L O
U I Y N F U I C T T L L X U
U M E A F F C C N R A L L L
U A L E Q O G I K B O J K D
Y X L D B I M W E B C X D G
I G O I A D Z S W F A D C N
U A V H A R A A P M Q L C V
W I W B J B J J A T Q T L P

Answer on page 238

Vowel Maze

Search this box of letters and list all the vowels you find in the blank spaces below to complete the phrase that describes a pretty animal you can ride.

W	R	E	T	L	P
A	S	F	G	H	J
K	L	Z	V	U	N
M	Q	W	R	T	I
S	U	F	N	P	M
W	J	O	F	E	K

B _ _ _ _ T _ F _ L   H _ R S _

30

Brr, Cold!

Put the article of clothing that would keep you warm of each body part in the crossword puzzle below.

across
1 Feet
2 Head

DOWN
1 Neck
3 Hands

Answer on page 238

Decode-a-Riddle

Use the code key below to decode and solve this riddle.

! = A	* = H	> = O	? = V
@ = B	(= I	[= P	/ = W
# = C	+ = J	] = Q	\ = X
$ = D	) = K	" = R	} = Y
% = E	; = L	" = S	{ = Z
^ = F	: = M	' = T	
& = G	< = N	' = U	

W H A T   K I N D O F

F L O W E R   D O E S

E V E R Y O N E

H A V E ?

T W O   L I P S

Double Boats

Can you find the two pictures that are exactly alike?

Answer on page 239

Situational

Can you make at least **25** or more words from this word?

SITUATIONAL

_____   _____

_____   _____

_____   _____

_____   _____

_____   _____

_____   _____

_____   _____

_____   _____

_____   _____

_____   _____

_____   _____

Answer on page 239

Ferris Wheel

Follow the path from **Start** to **Finish** to go around the Ferris Wheel.

35

Relationships

Use the pictures below to complete this crossword puzzle.

Answer on page 240

On the Road

Solve this rebus puzzle to find out the name of something that would be on the road.

-G + [x-ray] -R-AY +

-P-N + [cabin] -IN + [mermaid]

-R-MAID + [beet] -URNIP + [eggs]

-GG + [rabbit] -ABBIT

_ _ _ _ _ _

_ _ _ _ _

Going to the City

Find **three sets of two objects** that rhyme
with each other.

Answer on page 240

The Pet Shop

Search, find, and circle these 10 things.

WITCH'S HAT
COMPASS
STOP LIGHT

APPLE
DONUT
JACK-O'-LANTERN
KEYBOARD

MUSHROOM
HOCKEY STICK
TOOL BELT

Answer on page 240

Skating Fun

Find **10** differences between the picture on the top and the one on the bottom.

40

Word Scramble

Unscramble each of these words, using the clues.

NEFDIR
(Buddy, pal)

_ _ _ _ _ _

LITSEHO
(Not friendly)

_ _ _ _ _ _ _

AELNCRE
(Fresher, not dirty)

_ _ _ _ _ _ _

ENDCOS
(Not first)

_ _ _ _ _ _

IPNOTRO
(Part, piece)

_ _ _ _ _ _ _

TKAACT
(Assault)

_ _ _ _ _ _

EWOHRS
(Sprinkle)

_ _ _ _ _ _

ITRNAUC
(Drape)

_ _ _ _ _ _ _

41

Answer on page 241

Indoor Sports

Find these indoor sports in the word search.
Look up, down, backward, forward, and diagonally.

VOLLEYBALL
DODGEBALL
RACQUETBALL
SWIMMING
RUNNING
ICE SKATING

GYMNASTICS
TABLE TENNIS
POOL
YOGA

V	T	S	C	I	T	S	A	N	M	Y	G	G	D
B	A	R	Z	C	Y	N	P	F	R	D	N	R	O
A	B	W	Q	K	L	F	D	U	M	I	Q	I	D
O	L	V	C	Y	U	Z	N	D	T	D	C	R	G
D	E	P	A	Q	Z	N	N	A	B	G	A	C	E
X	T	X	M	G	I	C	K	E	R	C	L	T	B
G	E	V	N	N	O	S	P	A	Q	O	N	N	A
N	N	I	G	K	E	Y	R	U	O	Z	T	R	L
I	N	M	S	C	P	H	E	P	A	U	H	X	L
M	I	B	I	Q	U	T	R	D	L	Y	X	U	B
M	S	L	L	A	B	Y	E	L	L	O	V	O	K
I	J	L	W	A	W	E	H	U	O	U	S	D	F
W	B	Q	L	M	K	A	J	K	H	T	X	U	Y
S	C	L	X	K	A	E	S	W	H	O	T	J	Z

42

Haunted House

Follow the path from **Start** to **Finish** to go from the bottom of the haunted house to the top.

Answer on page 241

Where's the Party?

Unscramble thee types of parties on the blanks below and then place them in this crossword puzzle.

ACROSS
1 NVREIANRYAS

_____

2 PTMSIBA

_____

3 TEWES XSIEETN

_____

4 RAB TVHMIAZ

_____

DOWN
5 DWEDGIN

_____

6 TRHDBIYA

_____

7 DUATAGNROI

_____

8 MERETIERTN

_____

Answer on page 242

Decode-a-Riddle

Write the letter that comes **AFTER** each letter shown below to decode and solve this riddle.

H E   X N T   O T S   Z

A K T D   G Z S   H M S N

S G D   Q D C   R D Z

V G Z S   C N D R   H S

A D B N L D ?

V D S

Double Squirrels

Can you find the two pictures that are exactly alike?

Answer on page 242

Flabbergasted

Can you make **15** or more words of
5 or more letters from the following word?

FLABBERGASTED

_____ _____

_____ _____

_____ _____

_____ _____

_____ _____

_____ _____

_____ _____

_____ _____

_____ _____

_____ _____

_____ _____

_____ _____

_____ _____

_____ _____

Robot Maze

Follow the path from **Start** to **Finish** to
get the robots to the finish line.

Answer on page 243

What does Baby need?

Use the pictures below to complete this crossword puzzle.

Answer on page 243

Telecom

Solve this rebus puzzle to find a form of communication.

Answer on page 243

Into the Forest

Find **two sets of two objects** that rhyme
with each other.

51

Outer Space

Search, find, and circle these 10 things.

CRAYONS IN BOX   LADYBUG   DICE
      BEAR   PIG   PRAIRIE DOG
  PALM TREE   WITCH   SNAKE
              GIRL WITH PIGTAILS

Answer on page 244

Back to School

Find 10 differences between the picture on the top and the one on the bottom.

Answer on page 244

Word Scramble

Unscramble each of these words, using the clues.

DINECMIE
(Makes you better)

_ _ _ _ _ _ _ _

KMKESILHA
(Ice-cream drink)

_ _ _ _ _ _ _ _ _

RHETCEA
(Learning professional)

_ _ _ _ _ _ _

RERPNPASW
(Printed current events)

_ _ _ _ _ _ _ _ _

SMTASTRE
(Where one sleeps)

_ _ _ _ _ _ _ _

DYWBRAOA
(Where plays are performed)

_ _ _ _ _ _ _ _

NSTREMO
(Scary creature)

_ _ _ _ _ _ _

MEILACMORC
(Sells ads)

_ _ _ _ _ _ _ _ _ _

Answer on page 244

In the City

Find these things that have to do with the city.
Look up, down, backward, forward, and diagonally.

Skyscraper   Tourist
Bridge   Biker
Building   Museum
Taxi   Sightseeing
Construction   Train

I	M	M	R	Q	R	M	S	J	R	T	D	V	R	A
N	X	X	G	N	J	L	W	E	B	I	K	E	R	T
Z	O	S	R	N	J	Y	P	R	T	D	W	F	P	L
W	A	I	I	V	I	A	S	S	Z	J	A	K	W	L
V	Q	T	T	G	R	D	I	U	B	K	M	K	T	I
P	N	O	B	C	H	R	L	Z	M	L	Q	D	L	J
E	W	G	S	K	U	T	T	I	M	N	Q	B	M	N
V	Z	Y	P	O	U	R	S	M	U	Z	M	K	U	S
I	K	S	T	U	J	G	T	E	U	B	F	B	T	W
S	T	G	R	N	D	E	A	S	E	E	R	D	C	Q
Z	R	Q	K	S	R	T	T	D	N	I	S	Z	D	C
T	G	H	C	T	E	Y	K	R	D	O	N	U	O	N
R	W	U	T	A	X	I	V	G	A	K	C	G	M	E
W	T	O	C	F	W	A	E	I	X	I	Y	K	O	L
J	V	C	X	K	S	G	W	F	M	T	N	Y	C	A

55

Odd Stuff

Replace every letter in the puzzle with the one that comes **before** it in the alphabet to find out why the man is so upset.

A B C D E F G H I J K L M
N O P Q R S T U V W X Y Z

U I F S F

J T

B

G M Z

J O

N Z

T P V Q

___ ___ ___ ___ ___

___ ___ ___ ___ ___ ___!

Answer on page 245

It's all Relative

Use the clues below to complete this crossword puzzle.

ACROSS
3 Second____, once removed
6 Child of one's child
9 Your parent's sister
10 Female sibling
11 Female parent
12 Your mother's mother

DOWN
1 Male sibling
2 Male child
4 Your father's father
5 Your parent's brother
7 Female child
8 Male parent

Answer on page 245

Decode-a-Message

Use the code key below to find something
that has to do with another world.

A=6	F=1	M=2	P=5	T=10
C=9	I=4	N=14	R=7	U=13
E=12	L=8	O=11	S=3	

$\overline{6}$ $\overline{8}$ $\overline{4}$ $\overline{12}$ $\overline{14}$ $\overline{3}$ $\overline{1}$ $\overline{7}$ $\overline{11}$ $\overline{2}$

$\overline{11}$ $\overline{13}$ $\overline{10}$ $\overline{12}$ $\overline{7}$ $\overline{3}$ $\overline{5}$ $\overline{6}$ $\overline{9}$ $\overline{12}$

Answer on page 245

Which is Witch?

Can you find two pictures that are exactly alike?

Answer on page 245

Encyclopedia

Can you make **15** or more words of
5 or more letters from the following word?

ENCYCLOPEDIA

_____   _____

Answer on page 246

Tree House

Follow the path from **Start** to **Finish** to get from the bottom of the tree to the tree house.

Face the Music

Use the pictures below to complete this crossword puzzle.

Answer on page 246

Inside Room

Solve this rebus puzzle to find out the name
of something that would be in a room.

- BULB +

- M - MER +

- A - XI +

- OCO - LATE

Zoo Mania

Find **three sets of two objects** that rhyme
with each other.

Answer on page 247

Playground

Search, find, and circle these **10** things.

WHISTLE
BASEBALL BAT
WATER BOTTLE

MP3 PLAYER
BASEBALLS (2)
YELLOW HAT
SKATEBOARD

LOST SNEAKER
FOOTBALL
TEDDY BEAR

Answer on page 247

Life on Mars

Find **10** differences between the picture on the top and the one on the bottom.

Answer on page 247

Word Scramble

Unscramble each of these words, using the clues.

SYEA
(Simple to do)

_ _ _ _

AEKC
(With frosting)

_ _ _ _

ERDA
(Do this with a book)

_ _ _ _

YAPL
(Enjoy a game)

_ _ _ _

ONRH
(Beep! beep! in a car)

_ _ _ _

SAERE
(Rub out)

_ _ _ _ _

KATCR
(A train runs on this)

_ _ _ _ _

DISBR
(They fly in the sky)

_ _ _ _ _

Weddings

Find these words that have to do with weddings in this word search. Look up, down, backward, forward, and diagonally.

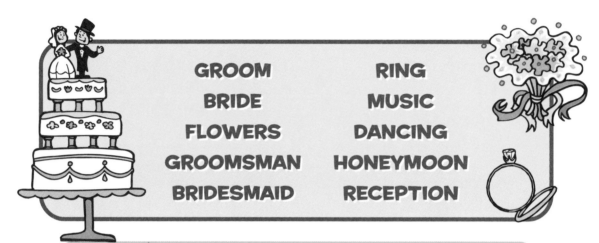

GROOM
BRIDE
FLOWERS
GROOMSMAN
BRIDESMAID

RING
MUSIC
DANCING
HONEYMOON
RECEPTION

```
P A X O Z O O F W N P Z S Q C
T B F N I G R O O M S M A N S
L T H F V E F D F S K A K K N
R C A O N O I T P E C E R A R
D N O H N I T D N B G E T T I
B I B L O E A S R C L A T E N
I Q A J T N Y I R G W R S F G
S V G M C I D M M E S V A Q N
C W Q I S E M N O G W U Y F P
X R N V T E D L M O J O A X L
K G S U K L D O O Z N G L Y X
I I J O S I Q I O G B A T F Q
M U S I C N M N R C O Z Y U W
K A H Y N D O I G B P P F B J
T O T X V E E V J H I C P R J
```

Odd Maze

Begin at **Start** and make your way to **Finish** by jumping from one odd number to the next. Move only on odd, not even, numbers. You can go **UP** and **DOWN**—not diagonally

Start

1	6	2	6	2	6	4	8
5	3	4	8	4	8	2	6
2	9	2	3	1	5	4	8
8	7	5	9	8	7	5	2
6	4	4	4	6	2	3	6
2	4	6	2	6	8	7	2
8	6	8	4	6	2	9	3
2	8	8	6	4	6	4	7

Finish

69

Musical Types

Use the clues below to complete this crossword puzzle.

ACROSS
1 Singers perform
6 Music only, no voices
8 ___ and roll
9 Classical singers
10 From all over the globe

DOWN
2 Symphony orchestra
3 Acousitc guitar with lyrics
4 ___-hop
5 Mix of rock and jazz
7 Swings

Answer on page 248

Decode-a-Riddle

Use the code key below to decode and solve this riddle.

1=A	8=H	15=O	22=V
2=B	9=I	16=P	23=W
3=C	10=J	17=Q	24=X
4=D	11=K	18=R	25=Y
5=E	12=L	19=S	26=Z
6=F	13=M	20=T	
7=G	14=N	21=U	

```
___  ___  __  ___    ___  ___  ___  ___    ___  ___
23    8    1   20      7   15    5   19     21    16

     ___  ___  ___    ___  ___  ___  ___  ___
      2    21   20     14    5   22    5    18        ?

___  ___  ___  ___  ___    ___  ___  ___  ___
 3    15   13    5   19      4    15   23   14


     ___  ___  ___  ___    ___  ___  ___
      25   15   21   18      1    7    5
```

Double Digits

Can you find the two pictures that are exactly alike?

Answer on page 249

Theatrical

Can you make **50** words or more from this word?

(50 blank lines arranged in two columns for answers)

73

Baseball Maze

Follow the path from **Start** to **Finish** to get around the bases to home plate.

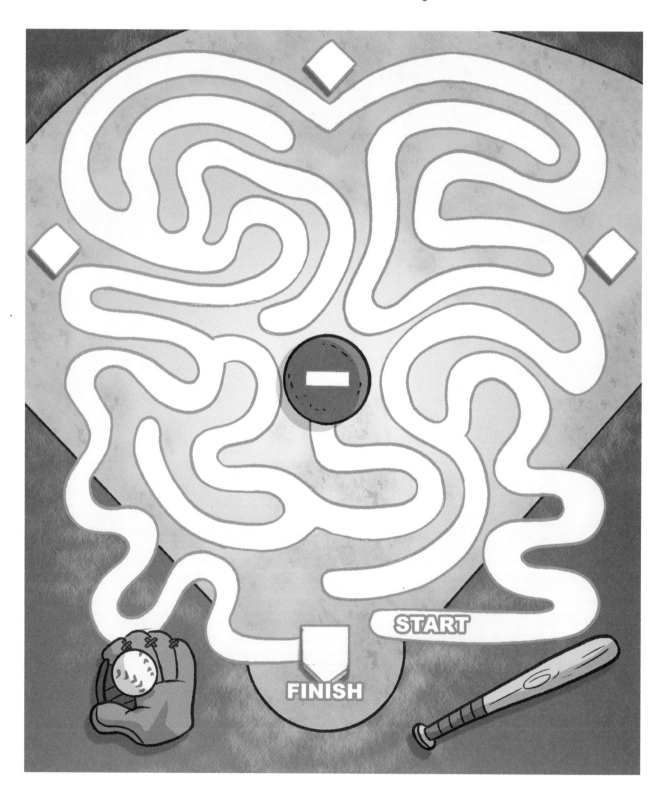

74

Things That Go!

Use the pictures below to complete this crossword puzzle.

ACROSS
1
3
7
8
9

DOWN
1
2
4
5
6

Answer on page 249

Sweet Treat

Solve this rebus puzzle to discover a sweet treat.

Answer on page 250

Matching Rhymes

Draw a line between the words in the first column
that rhyme with words in the second column.

FISH	SQUEAL
PLAY	SCREEN
BOW	WISH
SEAT	GREED
SING	STAY
BROWN	BRAKE
DEAL	COW
MAKE	SWING
READ	DOWN
GREEN	SWEET

Answer on page 250

Butterfly Beauties

Search, find and circle these **10** things.

FIRE HYDRANT
STOP SIGN
RED FLOWER

SNAKE
TOP HAT
DOG
TELESCOPE

BEACH BALL
PICNIC BASKET
CAMERA

Answer on page 250

Food Fight!

Find **10** differences between the picture on the top and the one on the bottom.

Answer on page 250

Word Scramble

Unscramble each of these words, using the clues.

FITNEYID
(To name or recognize)

_ _ _ _ _ _ _ _

VIMCOREAW
(Oven for fast cooking)

_ _ _ _ _ _ _ _ _

SEATDINC
(A far way to go)

_ _ _ _ _ _ _ _

NITLARBIL
(Bright, very smart)

_ _ _ _ _ _ _ _ _

CHEARSER
(Look up)

_ _ _ _ _ _ _ _

CITEURODN
(Meet, start)

_ _ _ _ _ _ _ _ _

DOTRUCCNO
(Leader of a train or orchestra)

_ _ _ _ _ _ _ _ _

RAPTOPOHGH
(Picture)

_ _ _ _ _ _ _ _ _ _

Answer on page 251

Well-Known Authors

Find these well-known authors in the word search.
Look up, down, backward, forward, and diagonally.

Hemingway
Cummings
Dickinson
Anderson
Alcott

Carroll
Hitchcock
London
Shakespeare
Whitman

```
R  D  H  F  V  M  O  W  G  U  O  R  X  I  C  Y  P  W  V  X
G  P  S  S  C  O  T  Y  D  Q  Q  O  O  P  K  S  F  V  P  G
S  B  Q  G  H  E  D  H  L  T  H  K  O  B  J  O  M  M  M  L
P  U  K  J  E  A  U  W  R  Z  I  Q  W  G  J  P  N  O  Y  W
O  J  R  C  Q  Z  K  N  I  H  Z  E  V  U  E  N  H  Q  O  T
F  O  R  U  K  P  F  E  F  M  W  I  P  N  K  O  E  L  V  F
N  O  P  Y  A  K  W  G  S  M  D  P  R  J  C  U  M  P  L  P
Y  Y  L  L  N  S  M  L  Q  P  Z  D  T  G  O  S  I  P  A  X
L  B  C  A  R  R  O  L  L  B  E  N  F  W  C  V  N  J  X  F
H  L  T  L  M  O  J  N  M  O  A  A  R  U  H  H  G  D  C  B
J  G  T  B  K  C  S  D  N  M  N  D  R  O  C  A  W  L  Q  I
Q  S  Z  I  E  Y  N  D  T  A  E  D  P  E  T  F  A  U  Q  D
U  D  U  O  R  V  U  I  I  W  R  E  O  S  I  V  Y  C  S  I
C  G  Q  P  X  C  H  U  O  E  S  Y  Z  N  H  N  B  G  D  C
F  Z  N  T  O  W  C  L  O  R  Q  F  T  J  F  K  N  V  A  K
R  L  B  B  S  D  R  P  F  Q  T  W  X  X  X  I  I  Z  W  I
Q  Q  B  G  S  K  V  I  B  A  V  B  R  J  M  D  J  R  O  N
G  D  N  N  O  S  R  E  D  N  A  I  A  M  I  D  D  R  E  S
O  T  A  Z  D  R  G  G  D  B  Y  I  U  X  I  J  X  T  S  O
G  H  G  T  T  O  C  L  A  A  D  C  S  X  E  F  Y  E  F  N
```

81

Word Chains

One word is shown in each category. List two other words in that category so that each word starts with the last letter of the word before it.

Flowers:

DAFFODIL, L _____ , _____

Musical Instruments:

HARP, P _____ , _____

Holidays:

HALLOWEEN, N _____ , _____

Clothing:

HAT, T _____ , _____

U.S. Cities:

HOUSTON, N _____ , _____

82

Cryptids—Do They Exist?

Use the clues below to complete this crossword puzzle.

ACROSS
- 2 Mysterious Native American creature
- 4 Single horned horse
- 8 Creature from Garden State
- 10 Himalayan bigfoot
- 11 Aliens with big eyes, round heads
- 12 Frozen creature of stories

DOWN
- 1 Lake monster of Scotland
- 3 Mexican creature of legend
- 5 Creature who swims in Lake Champlain
- 6 Sea creature with tentacles
- 7 Half-fish, half-female human
- 9 Man-ape of the woods

83

Decode-a-Message

Use the code key below to find a message
that has to do with skydiving.

E=2   O=6   T=9
I=4   R=1   V=3
N=5   S=8   W=7

$\underset{4}{\_\_}\underset{9}{\_\_}\underset{8}{\_\_}\text{,} \quad \underset{5}{\_\_}\underset{6}{\_\_}\underset{7}{\_\_} \quad \underset{6}{\_\_}\underset{1}{\_\_}$

$\underset{5}{\_\_}\underset{2}{\_\_}\underset{3}{\_\_}\underset{2}{\_\_}\underset{1}{\_\_}\text{.}$

Answer on page 252

Word Game

Look at the letters in the box below. Figure out what toy includes this word and fill it in on the lines below.

____ ____ ____ ___ __ __

____ ___ ___ ___ ___ ___

Answer on page 252

Pictures and Words

Spell out the objects in each of these pictures. Then see if you can make **25** or more words from the letters.

_ _ _ _   _ _ _ _ _ _   _ _ _ _ _

Answer on page 252

Surfing Away

Follow the path from **Start** to **Finish** to help the surfer get to the island.

All Sports

Use the pictures below to complete this crossword puzzle.

Answer on page 253

Rebus Riddle Riot

Solve this rebus puzzle to find the answer to the following riddle:

WHAT DID THE NUMBER ZERO (0) SAY TO THE NUMBER EIGHT (8)?

Going Fishing

Find **three sets of two objects** that rhyme with each other.

Answer on page 253

Shopping Spree

Search, find, and circle these **10** things.

TENNIS RACKET
CANDY CANE
RACCOON

BASEBALL BAT
DOMINO
PUZZLE PIECE
NUTCRACKER

ENVELOPE
WALKIE TALKIE
CD

Answer on page 253

Take Off!

Find **10** differences between the picture on the top and the one on the bottom.

Answer on page 254

Word Scramble

Unscramble each of these words, using the clues.

SOCIPT
(Subjects)

_ _ _ _ _ _

NIETONS
(Stress, pressure)

_ _ _ _ _ _ _

EMLPOTEC
(Finished, all done)

_ _ _ _ _ _ _ _

RUELUCT
(Music, art, dance)

_ _ _ _ _ _ _

UTSSAT
(Situation, condition)

_ _ _ _ _ _

LGTURESG
(Difficult time)

_ _ _ _ _ _ _ _

ETCKTI
(Gets you into an event)

_ _ _ _ _ _

PLEHED
(Assisted)

_ _ _ _ _ _

93

Garden

Find these things that have to do with a garden in the word search. Look up, down, backward, forward, and diagonally.

WHEELBARROW   SOIL

WATERING CAN   GLOVE

PLANTS   SHEERS

FLOWERS   FERTILIZER

WEEDER   RAKE

R Y Y R D P M M L R X L H
E X S L K B P T X E K W N
Z W E I Y C I L L G S Q A
I H F O W M K W A O O Q C
L E B S W E B M D N W Q G
I E D V K M E A M P T S N
T L S S X S B D D P H S I
R B F K F X B T E E U N R
E A Y A G L O V E R S Z E
F R O L S H N R W F P Z T
J R J L U I S F U S V C A
R O H K R A K E T J G Y W
G W N O C S R E W O L F Q

Figure Out the Phrases

Each one of the pictures below is part of a common phrase. First, figure out what the pictures show. Then write the phrases below.

Answer on page 254

How are You Feeling?

Use the clues below to complete this crossword puzzle.

ACROSS
1 Feeling great
3 I need to cool off.
4 Let's eat!
6 Thrilled
7 Ready for a nap

DOWN
2 I'm so mad!
3 Anxious
5 A bit blue

Answer on page 255

Decode-a-Riddle

Write the letter that comes **THREE LETTERS AFTER** each letter shown below to decode and solve this riddle.

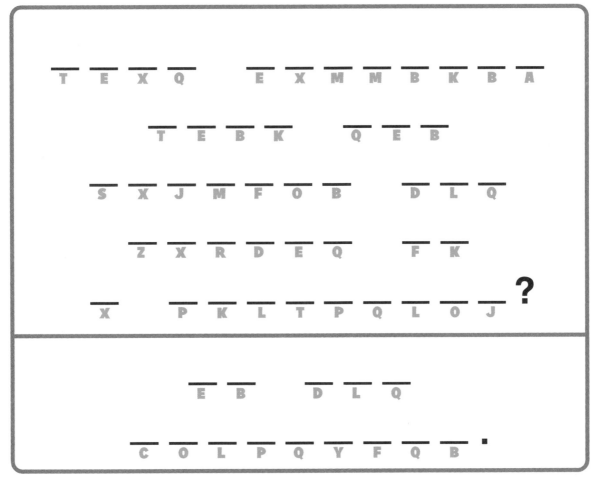

T E X Q   E X M M B K B A

T E B K   Q E B

S X J M F O B   D L Q

Z X R D E Q   F K

X   P K L T P Q L O J ?

E B   D L Q

C O L P Q Y F Q B .

Double Bedroom

Can you find the two pictures that are exactly alike?

Answer on page 255

Bottomless

Can you make **15** or more words of
5 or more letters from the following word?

BOTTOMLESS

Train Maze

Follow the path from **Start** to **Finish** to
help the train get to the station.

100

Lights! Camera! Action!

Use the pictures below to complete this crossword puzzle.

ACROSS

2   3   7   9   10   11

DOWN

1   4   5   6   8   12

"Arr"-Great-Rebus

Solve this rebus puzzle to find the answer to the following riddle:

HOW MUCH DOES A PIRATE PAY FOR CORN?

Answer on page 256

Treasure Hunt

Find **two sets of two objects** that rhyme with each other.

Answer on page 256

Grocery Store

Search, find, and circle these 10 things.

BOWLING BALL   **ICE CUBE**   **BIRDS' NEST**
SNAKE   **DRUM**   **GOLF CLUB**
BASKETBALL   **SPACESHIP**   **BOWLING PIN**
    TIC-TAC-TOE GAME

Answer on page 257

Bake a Cake!

Find 10 differences between the picture on the top and the one on the bottom.

105

Word Scramble

Unscramble each of these words, using the clues.

NILOVI
(Instrument)

_ _ _ _ _ _

RFNCEA
(Country)

_ _ _ _ _ _

VACENR
(Found underground)

_ _ _ _ _ _

TLTBOE
(Drink receptacle)

_ _ _ _ _ _

RCADS
(Game)

_ _ _ _ _

PANA
(Town in California)

_ _ _ _

Answer on page 257

Doctor's Visit

Find these things in the word search that have to do with a doctor's visit. Look up, down, backward, forward, and diagonally.

Thermometer	Stethoscope
Scale	Depressor
Medicine	Bandage
Nurse	Lollipop
Immunization	Exam

```
V E H P O C H Z H H O F B T T A V M S W
A E P C I R X O Y U U B C A H N M U O Z
Q S A I V V N R I C B W G R N L N M L A
Q R B E Q A Q H B C V H K X C D B D X C
A U W J P B W N H E G M A G M G A A E D
O N Z S E Y H G Z E S P E M C A H G W E
Z R E T E M O M R E H T G D L B O F E P
U X T P L L V Q C R K I H X I S E S W R
A G Y Q J H B W S I J M I H P C B B Z E
T P Y N E W O O J O F M G X U N I H A S
S T E T H O S C O P E U P N K V P N K S
S A L W A K E L L B E N F L G N D D E O
P D I Q B U B H Y O Y I H G B Z E F Z R
A Y Z Q X Q S X T U B Z K I H C M H Y M
M L O L L I P O P A G A L J L D H A B Z
X M N O P G J P V H D T X E S K U Y Z M
J A E L A C S V K A D I C J E G F D A K
R X H W H J X B J Y S O F Z S G S R S G
S E Z B M O E C W O B N Z I C Y N R D Z
Z L Z H Y W M V W Y X W V B W A F A E J
```

Answer on page 257

Ping-Pong Mix-Up

The pages in this book are mixed up.
Put them back in order so the story makes sense.

1 The other player wins!

2 Two people decide to play ping pong.

3 One player misses a shot.

_____
_____
_____
_____
_____
_____

4 They pick up the paddles.

5 They play ping pong.

6 One person points to a ping pong table.

Answer on page 258

Around the World

Put the ethnicity of each food item in the crossword puzzle below.

across
1 Gnocchi
2 Sushi
3 Enchilada

DOWN
4 Moo shu
5 Jerk chicken
6 Tandoori Chicken
7 Coq au vin
8 Ropa vieja

Decode-a-Riddle

Write the letter that comes **TWO LETTERS AFTER** each letter shown below to decode and solve this riddle.

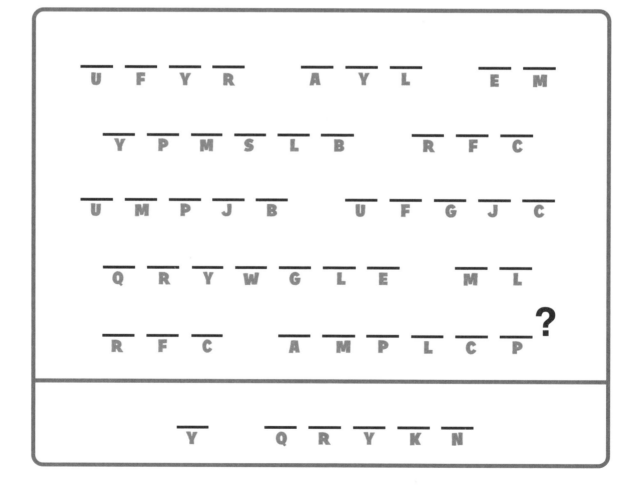

U F Y R   A Y L   E M

Y P M S L B   R F C

U M P J B   U F G J C

Q R Y W G L E   M L

R F C   A M P L C P ?

Y   Q R Y K N

110

Answer on page 258

Double Smiles

Can you find the two pictures that are exactly alike?

Skywriting

Can you make **25 or more** words from the following word?

SKYWRITING

Answer on page 259

Picnic Maze

Follow the path from **Start** to **Finish** to help
the ant get to the picnic basket.

FINISH

START

113

Winter Wonderland

Use the pictures below to complete this crossword puzzle.

ACROSS

2
7
8
9

DOWN

1
2
3
4
5
6

Answer on page 259

Snack Time

Solve this rebus puzzle find the name of a fun snack.

Car Race

Find **three sets of two objects** that rhyme with each other.

Answer on page 260

City Living

Search, find, and circle these **10** things.

TOY DUMP TRUCK
DUCK
DALMATIAN

COWBOY BOOT
SCREWDRIVER
PRETZEL
WASHING MACHINE

KAYAK
TEDDY BEAR
GOLF CLUB

Poolside Fun

Find **10** differences between the picture on the top and the one on the bottom.

118

Word Scramble

Unscramble each of these words, using the clues.

LDMAANITA
(Spotty dog)

_ _ _ _ _ _ _ _ _

RCEMUYR
(Planet)

_ _ _ _ _ _ _

MRCAEP
(Outdoor recreationalist)

_ _ _ _ _ _

NABAAN
(Fruit)

_ _ _ _ _ _

THEBORRS
(Familial males)

_ _ _ _ _ _ _ _

YNORCA
(Writing instrument)

_ _ _ _ _ _

SOSNSAE
(Weather changes)

_ _ _ _ _ _ _

DITNERESP
(In charge)

_ _ _ _ _ _ _ _ _

119

Types of Dinosaurs

Find these types of dinosaurs in the word search.
Look up, down, backward, forward, and diagonally.

Archaeopteryx
Allosaurus
Cretaceous
Utahraptor
Stegosaurus
Apatosaurus
Triceratops
Deinonychus
Parasaurolophus
Tyrannosaurus
Oviraptor

```
S R K G H X I Z D R Y G D Q F T C A E M
G F K M K J Y M C M O E U C T I R W O D
R N Y J J M D R Z R I T H E T F J Y Q T
I U I T R F T G E N E D P Y F N V E G W
Z R X Z K H V G O T S T R A J N P K N B
Z O S B J T N N I P P A A J R C L N R Q
L T Z U L I Y J O V N O L C H H A V L A
Y P K X R C J T T N L D E S E F A J B N
P A A W H U A E O V H F A A C O O T N C
Y R P U W R A S R L E N E L H M U T U X
N I S P E O A S N M F Z N D W C G S E P
B V Q C G U D T O Q A H A D H M R E H P
L O I B R V C Q M G A T M J X I C A M K
Q R V U Q M M L E Z E I L H K M V W U I
T W S R X C A Z Q C V T G T M B D T S R
C S S U R U A S O L L A S M M A B C Z Y
P A R A S A U R O L O P H U S C Q P S M
H W Y N K O D W A U G U T I A Q L X D P
C F X K C X A P A T O S A U R U S K A E
H P X W K D P Y V U C R X K Q D R P W S
```

120

Double Words

Each of the words described in the clues are made up of the same word twice. Write the correct words in the spaces next to the clues.

Type of joke _____ - _____

Toy that goes up and down _____ - _____

Ballerina's skirt _____ - _____

Baby expression for cut or bruise _____ - _____

Not great, not bad _____ - _____

To go wild about something _____ - _____

121

World Capitals

Use the clues below to complete this crossword puzzle.

across

5 Italy
7 Belgium
8 Ireland
9 Austria
10 Egypt
11 United Kingdom
12 India

DOWN

1 France
2 Germany
3 United States
4 Greece
6 Spain

Answer on page 261

Decode-a-Riddle

Write the letter that comes **TWO LETTERS BEFORE** each letter shown below to decode and solve this riddle.

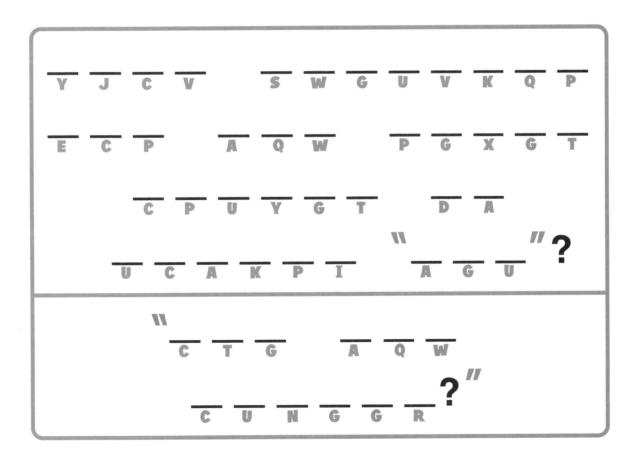

WHAT   QUESTION   CAN   YOU   NEVER
(Y J C V) (S W G U V K Q P) (E C P) (A Q W) (P G X G T)

ANSWER   BY
(C P U Y G T) (D A)

SAYING   "YES"?
(U C A K P I) (A G U)

"ARE   YOU
(C T G) (A Q W)

ASLEEP?"
(C U N G G R)

Monumental

Solve this rebus puzzle to learn the name of one of the presidents honored on Mount Rushmore.

-S-E+O+

7 -N+

-B-E

- - - - - - - - - - - - - - - -

Answer on page 262

Noteworthy

Can you make **25** or more words from the following word?

NOTEWORTHY

Motorcycle Derby

Follow the path from **Start** to **Finish** to
help bikers get to the finish line.

Answer on page 262

Let's Go to the Beach!

Use the pictures below to complete this crossword puzzle.

127

Water Rebus

Solve this rebus puzzle to find something that has to do with the water.

Picture Rhymes

Draw a line between the objects in the first column that rhyme
with the words in the second column.

COLUMN 1   **COLUMN 2**

PLANE

FELT

CREPES

MAN

HAIR

Answer on page 263

Swimming Fun

Search, find, and circle these 10 things.

CALCULATOR   POLAR BEAR   WEATHER VANE
FEATHER DUSTER   HIPPOPOTAMUS   RECORD PLAYER
METAL DETECTOR   TAPE MEASURE   PENGUINS (2)

JACK-IN-THE-BOX

Answer on page 263

Ready, Set, Go!

Find 10 differences between the picture on the top and the one on the bottom.

Answer on page 263

Word Scramble

Unscramble each of these words, using the clues.

HEPAC
(Fruit)

_ _ _ _ _

OMRES
(Code)

_ _ _ _ _

LSAAS
(Spicy sauce)

_ _ _ _ _

NYNAN
(Kid watcher)

_ _ _ _ _

EPLTA
(Eat off)

_ _ _ _ _

EDATR
(Swap)

_ _ _ _ _

Answer on page 264

Golf

Find these things that have to do with golf in this word search.
Look up, down, backward, forward, and diagonally.

Club   Par
Wood   Score
Swing   Green
Course   Birdie
Ball   Iron

F R P X A E K O C P K G G
D F J C E L X W O W A P J
L S T E S W N R U N C R B
A K Z L L A B K R P A X G
I P L A N V J V S I M C C
F A Y E B Q W W E N T K O
V C E U N H W O F O I S S
D R L E B O Z L U J J O C
G C L W O I I R O N B X O
M F V D V V R R B X G A R
C O G C E M A D S E H N E
B C R P W X C B I P J G C
T J L S W I N G G E B H Y

133

Soup Time!

Starting at the arrow, write every other letter in the spaces below to find out something that has to do with soup.
Go around the circle in a clockwise direction.

G _ _   _ _

_ _ _ _ _

_ _ ' _   _ _ _ !

Answer on page 264

Animal Sounds

Put the animal sound of each animal listed in
the crossword puzzle below.

aCROSS
1 Cat
2 Bird

DOWN
3 Horse
4 Pig

Decode-a-Message

Use the code key below to find something that you would use for your face.

A=2 G=5 N=7 U=6
E=4 L=3 S=1

— — — — — — — — —
1   6   7   5   3   2   1   1   4   1

Answer on page 265

Under the Sea

Search, find, and circle these **10** things.

 DOG LAWNMOWER DENTURES
FOOTBALL CLOCK SNOWMAN
HEADPHONES PIZZA BOX TRUMPET
PAINTBRUSH

Answer on page 265

Particular

Can you make **25** or more words from this word?

PARTICULAR

PArt
Art PAr
tic
cArt

Answer on page 265

Penguin Pushover

Follow the path from **Start** to **Finish** to help the penguins get to the water.

139

Party Time

Use the pictures below to complete this crossword puzzle.

Answer on page 266

Football Fun

Solve this rebus puzzle to learn the name
of an exciting play in football.

Answer on page 266

Wedding Fun

Find **three sets of two objects** that rhyme with each other.

JUST MARRIED

Answer on page 266

Flower Shop

Search, find, and circle these **10** things.

LION   **ANCHOR**   **COW**
CHESS PIECE   **WINDMILL**   **BIPLANE**
ICE SKATES   **MOUSE**   **TREE ORNAMENT**
SNOW BLOWER

143

Answer on page 266

Construction Zone

Find **10** differences between the picture on the top and the one on the bottom.

Answer on page 267

Word Scramble

Unscramble each of these words, using the clues.

ITPSLAOH
(Place where sick people go)

_ _ _ _ _ _ _ _

TORNGEENAI
(Grandparent, parent, child)

_ _ _ _ _ _ _ _ _ _

ALGNIBZ
(On fire)

_ _ _ _ _ _ _

AMNOFIITORN
(Facts, knowledge)

_ _ _ _ _ _ _ _ _ _ _

RULANTA
(From the Earth)

_ _ _ _ _ _ _

ICLVANAR
(Rides, games, cotton candy)

_ _ _ _ _ _ _ _

FAITACRR
(Plane, jet, helicopter)

_ _ _ _ _ _ _ _

FSAERRTN
(Move, change, shift)

_ _ _ _ _ _ _ _

145

School Supplies

Find these school supplies in the word search. Look up, down, backward, forward, and diagonally.

Ruler   Calculator
Notebook   Backpack
Compass   Eraser
Pencil   Binder
Protractor   Marker

```
X P I R K G M I V X D R Z O
W L S K J O O D K P E R F I
N A P S O L O H C K Q E T E
P M L R A L I B R R M D I C
R E I D O P D A E W A N C O
O Z N L N T M N U T H I K H
T A V C O B R O Q L O B C V
A C D R I E F A C S R N A V
L S Q E Y L L K C E R B P K
U U I L E W T U S T Y X K K
C R X U T M Y A X G O N C M
L K I R I E R B L L P R A S
A V M B Y E Q Q F U F O B R
C D C H W H Y E H U A J Y W
```

Answer on page 267

Basketball Mix-Up

The pages in this book are mixed up.
Put them back in order so the story makes sense.

The game is over!

1

A basketball player misses the basket.

2

There are 3 seconds left in the game!

3

A basketball player runs down the court.

4

A basketball player shoots the ball.

5

There are 2 seconds left in the game!

6

You were Saying

Fill in the blanks below to complete this crossword puzzle.

ACROSS
1 Grizzly _____
2 Help _____
3 License to _____
4 _____ in the shallow end.

DOWN
2 Wash and _____
3 Park closes at _____
5 _____ or not
6 Seashells on the _____

Answer on page 268

Decode-a-Riddle

Write the letter that comes just **BEFORE** each letter
shown below to decode and solve this riddle.

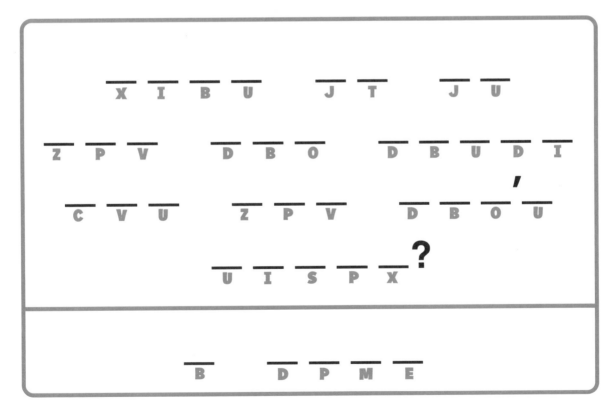

X I B U   J T   J U

Z P V   D B O   D B U D I

C V U   Z P V   D B O U'

U I S P X ?

B   D P M E

149

Double Cats

Can you find the two pictures that are exactly alike?

Answer on page 268

Frustration

Can you make **50** or more words from this word?

FRUSTRATION

_____ _____ _____

_____ _____ _____

_____ _____ _____

_____ _____ _____

_____ _____ _____

_____ _____ _____

_____ _____ _____

_____ _____ _____

_____ _____ _____

_____ _____ _____

_____ _____ _____

_____ _____ _____

_____ _____ _____

_____ _____ _____

151

Answer on page 268

Fish Maze

Follow the path from **Start** to **Finish** to
help the fish get through the coral.

Answer on page 269

Good Sports

Use the pictures below to complete this crossword puzzle.

Answer on page 269

Career

Solve this rebus puzzle to find something that has to do with a career.

Answer on page 269

Carnival night

Find **three sets of two objects** that rhyme with each other.

Answer on page 269

Happy Birthday to You!

Search, find, and circle these **10** things.

PAINTBRUSH
CHICKEN
FISH

FROG
PILLOW
HAMMER
JACK-IN-THE-BOX

ICE-CREAM CONE
TURTLE
TIRE

156

Answer on page 270

Getting Married

Find **10** differences between the picture on the top and the one on the bottom.

Word Scramble

Unscramble each of these words, using the clues.

SNATRERG
(Person who doesn't know someone)

_ _ _ _ _ _ _ _

LOHSACEE
(Tie this)

_ _ _ _ _ _ _ _

AVEBHE
(Act properly)

_ _ _ _ _ _

NUSHESIN
(Brightens the day)

_ _ _ _ _ _ _ _

OCTORES
(Motorized bike)

_ _ _ _ _ _ _

ARPDEA
(March in this)

_ _ _ _ _ _

NINRUGN
(Moving very fast)

_ _ _ _ _ _ _

PILREPYS
(Smooth, icy)

_ _ _ _ _ _ _ _

Answer on page 270

Weather

Find these words that have to do with the weather in the word search. Look up, down, backward, forward, and diagonally.

Humidity ✓   Tornado   Drizzle
Temperature   Thunderstorm Thermometer
Lightning   Overcast   Rainfall
              Doppler

```
T T Z G N G B C B W M H H R N
T M H E U A E Q M K O R V J L
I O R T R G X K R H H I D P Y
J M R O E U W L Q M G I L W
J Y T N T F T E L Z Z I R D B
X T S H A S W A H W M J L T N
C I J S E D R W R P C I U E R
O D T D Z R O E G E G O Q E A
D I S V F B M K D H P L W C I
O M A X D J T O T N O M O D N
P U C V S N K N M Y U N E H F
P H R J O B I U V E T H H T A
L A E H O N K G D G T Y T Y L
E I V F G R J F F U H E F C L
R I O G Z W G O K D B A R X D
```

159

Every Other Letter

Starting with the first letter, list every other letter in the spaces below to find out the name of something you wear to the beach.

B T A R T U H N I K N S G

B _ _ _ _ _ _ _   _ _ _ _ _ _

Answer on page 271

Magic

Use the clues below to complete this crossword puzzle.

ACROSS
3 Has one horn
6 Tiny, flying creature
7 Hero with sword and armor
8 Magic charm or curse

DOWN
1 Person of magic
2 Fire-breathing reptile
4 Where the king lives
5 Ugly creature who lives under bridges

Answer on page 271

Decode-a-Riddle

Use the code key below to decode and solve this riddle.

!= A	*= H	>= O	?= V
@= B	(= I	[= P	/= W
#= C	+= J	]= Q	\= X
$= D	)= K	"= R	}= Y
%= E	;= L	"= S	{= Z
^= F	:= M	'= T	
&= G	<= N	'= U	

A T   W H A T   T I M E
S H O U L D   Y O U
G O   T O   T H E
D E N T I S T ?

T O O T H   H U R T Y

Word Game

Look at the letters in the box below. Figure out what phrase uses this word and fill it in on the lines below.

___ ___ ___ ___ ___ ___ ___ ___ ___ ___

___ ___ ___ ___ ___ ___ ___ ___ ___ ___

___ ___ ___ ___ ___.

163

Answer on page 271

Quarantine

Can you make **25** words or more from this word?

QUARANTINE

_____   _____

_____   _____

_____   _____

_____   _____

_____   _____

_____   _____

_____   _____

_____   _____

_____   _____

_____   _____

_____   _____

_____   _____

Answer on page 272

Bear Ice Maze

Follow the path from **Start** to **Finish** to help the bear in pink get to the finish line.

Answer on page 272

Music to Your Ears

Use the pictures below to complete this crossword puzzle.

Answer on page 272

Sweet Stuff

Solve this rebus puzzle to find the name of something sweet.

-KE + -AP-

KIN + -IA - PER +

-A - K + -DL

_ _ _ _ _ _ _ _ _ _ _ _

Answer on page 272

School's Cool!

Find **three sets of two objects** that rhyme with each other.

Answer on page 273

Pumpkins

Search, find, and circle these **10** things.

SQUARE PUMPKIN
BASKETBALL
GOLDFISH

ORNAMENT
AIR PUMP
PUMPKIN COACH
SNAKE

ELECTRIC PLUG
DINNER FORK
DIVING SUIT

Answer on page 273

Dinosaur Duo

Find **10** differences between the picture on the top and the one on the bottom.

Answer on page 273

Word Scramble

Unscramble each of these words, using the clues.

IBGERD
(Takes you over water)

_ _ _ _ _ _

RTSGNI
(Tie stuff up with this)

_ _ _ _ _ _

PSCELUA
(Carries astronauts into space)

_ _ _ _ _ _ _

VIDERR
(Operates the car)

_ _ _ _ _ _

DGINUDP
(Smooth dessert)

_ _ _ _ _ _ _

UCSICR
(Big top fun)

_ _ _ _ _ _

ROCTOD
(Helps when you are sick)

_ _ _ _ _ _

NAPILOMC
(Criticize, find problems with)

_ _ _ _ _ _ _ _

Camping

Find these things that have to do with camping in the word search. Look up, down, backward, forward, and diagonally.

Tent
Lantern
Sleeping bag

Grill
Cooler
Flashlight
Compass

Backpack
Chair
Binoculars

```
E F G G Z V Q L N E I H I X H
P N Y F L U R L L I R G F F F
M B I H D O P N S J G S L B R
N P A R W J X U R A J A G Y C
I S B C T Y J O B E S C E F K
C T V H L V G D H T U S G R R
O O S W G P N G L S Y N R C I
R S M T P I A I O M X R A I A
V U K P P C G C G J I E L L H
O U Q E A F L K Y T L U N C
V Z E K T S I J V S N O C K P
P L A I O T S Y J O E O O I V
S Y Y F T T J U Z O T C N H D
E Y J R B I W C U Y G O I N X
F S D Y I C Y W P K K A B I Q
```

172

Amazing Phrases

The words in each two-word phrase below
both start with the same letter.

1. a small item displayed on a shelf
   or in a cabinet

   K_____ - K_____

2. to travel in a diagonal pattern

   Z_____ - Z_____

3. describes someone who can't
   really make up his mind

   W_____ - W_____

4. to change an opinion completely

   F_____ - F_____

5. just okay, not great

   S_____ - S_____

6. a ride in which two people take
   turns going up and down

   S_____ - S_____

Answer on page 274

Getting Dressed

Put the clothing item that goes with each body part in the crossword puzzle below.

ACROSS
1 Head
2 Chest
3 Body
4 Hands

DOWN
2 Feet
5 Legs

Answer on page 274

Decode-a-Message

Use the code key below to find a message
that has to do with lunchtime.

A=7 G=2 M=5 S=8
C=10 H=12 N=13 T=16
D=3 I=9 O=1 U=4
E=6 L=15 R=11 Y=14

I'M SO HUNGRY
 9 5 8 1 12 4 13 2 11 14

I COULD EAT
9 10 1 4 15 3   6 7 16

A HORSE.
7 12 1 11 8 6

175

Answer on page 274

Monkey Doubles

Can you find the two pictures that are exactly alike?

Answer on page 275

Valedictorian

Can you make **15** or more words of
5 or more letters from the following word?

VALEDICTORIAN

_____	_____

177

Outer Space

Follow the path from **Start** to **Finish** to help the rocket ship get to Earth.

Answer on page 275

Toys

Use the pictures below to complete this crossword puzzle.

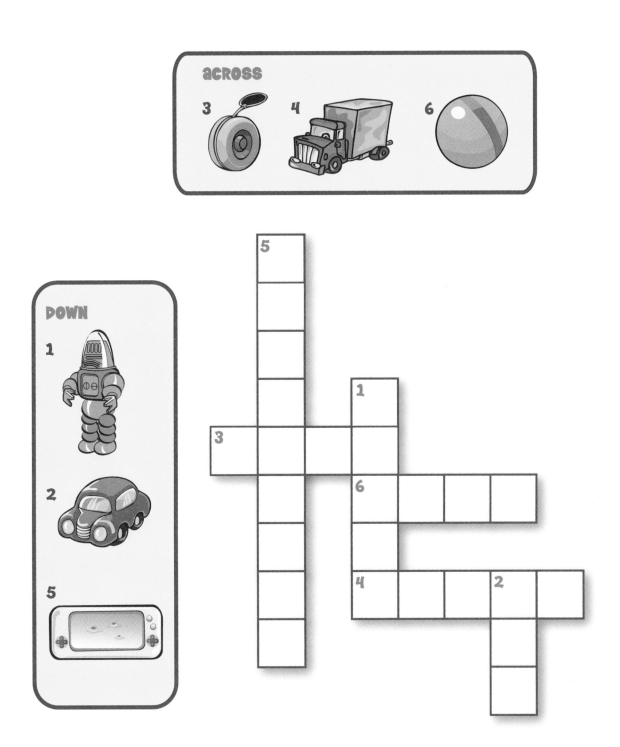

First Things First

Write the first letter of each object shown in the spaces below to spell out something that has to do with school.

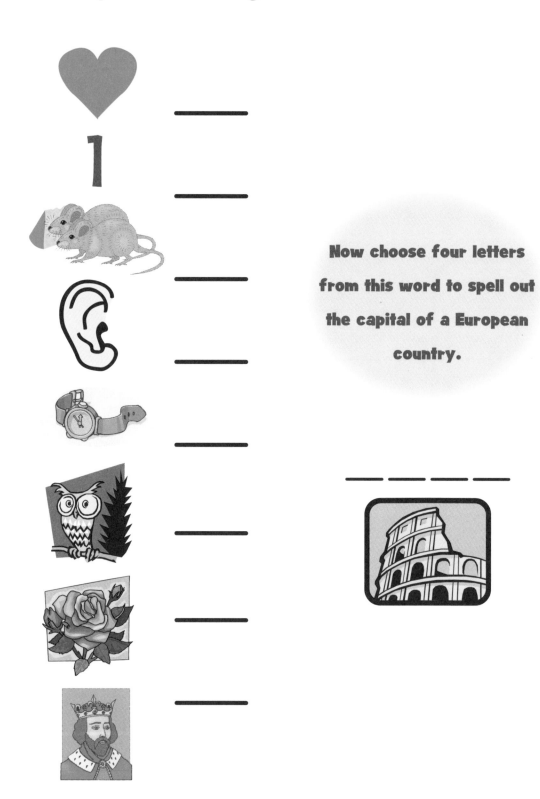

Now choose four letters from this word to spell out the capital of a European country.

Answer on page 276

Reach for the Beach!

Find **three sets of two objects** that rhyme
with each other.

A Day at the Zoo

Search, find, and circle these **10** things.

BALLOONS (2)   ICE-CREAM CONES (3)   PARROT
LEAVES (2)   TIGER   DOG
FROG   BANANAS (3)   CLOUDS (2)
FISH

Answer on page 276

Duck Pond

Find 10 differences between the picture on the top and the one on the bottom.

Answer on page 276

Word Scramble

Unscramble each of these words, using the clues.

USB
(Kid mover)

_ _ _

UIST
(Office wear)

_ _ _ _

TGIF
(To give)

_ _ _ _

NSKATIG
(Icy sport)

_ _ _ _ _ _ _

Bodies of Water

Find these bodies of water in the word search.
Look up, down, backward, forward, and diagonally.

Pacific
Atlantic
Mediterranean
Red

Arctic
Indian
Caribbean
Mississippi

Nile
Yukon

X Q N X W T R Z X Q L J A I
M P I I W K C C F G G I V P
O E Y S L D C I F I C A P P
M H D F B E R I W X B N U I
G G I I J W N U N L A P A S
N Y G V T B P A F E S T F S
I F W V C E C G B I L G N I
N W R O J O R B R A E S R S
A Y S A P L I R N C Y J E S
I Q M W R R C T A U U K C I
D A F E A C I D K N F C G M
N V K C T C T O E J E T F N
I X I F Z C N I N R A A K X
V Q T V F M J A C M Y P N Q

185

Teatime Mix-Up

The pages in this book are mixed up.
Put them back in order so the story makes sense.

A girl and her friend sit down for tea. **1**

A girl pours milk in her friend's cup of tea. **2**

A girl knocks on her friend's door. **3**

_____
_____
_____
_____
_____
_____

Both girls drink their tea! **4**

A girl asks her friend to come over her house. **5**

A girl pours her friend a cup of tea. **6**

Answer on page 277

Sauces

Put the sauce of each ingredient in the crossword puzzle below.

ACROSS
1 Eggs
2 Ribs
3 Hot wings

DOWN
4 Pasta
5 Turkey
6 Tortilla Chips

Answer on page 277

Decode-a-Riddle

Write the letter that comes **TWO LETTERS AFTER** each letter shown below to decode and solve this riddle.

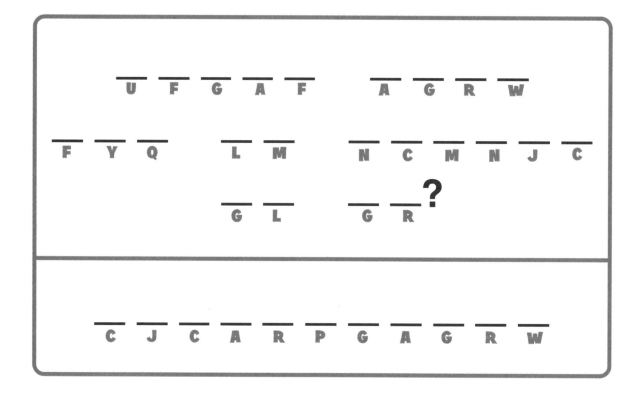

Answer on page 278

Let's Go Fly a Kite!

Search, find and circle these 10 things.

KANGAROO   TELESCOPE   SANTA CLAUS
STORK   ROWBOAT   LEPRECHAUN
ZEBRA   HOCKEY GOALIE   FLYING PIG
CHRISTMAS TREE

Unequivocally

Can you make **25** or more words from the following word?

UNEQUIVOCALLY

Answer on page 278

Snowmobile

Follow the path from **Start** to **Finish** to get the snowmobile to the finish line.

Answer on page 278

Birds of a Feather

Use the pictures below to complete this crossword puzzle.

Answer on page 279

Sweet Stuff

Solve this rebus puzzle to find the name of a dessert.

− CUMB − ER +

− I − LOT +

− T + − Y

_ _ _ _ _ _ _ _ _ _

Word Game

The things in this picture are each missing one very important element. Can you tell what?

_____

_____

_____

_____

194

Answer on page 279

First Day of School

Search, find, and circle these 10 things.

PRINCESS   GOLDFISH   PAINTBRUSH
PIZZA   RADIO   EARMUFFS
STAR   GUITAR   TRASH CAN
EXIT SIGN

Answer on page 279

Flamingo Frenzy

Find **10** differences between the picture on
the top and the one on the bottom.

Answer on page 280

Word Scramble

Unscramble each of these words, using the clues.

IVRER
(Body of water)

_ _ _ _ _

KAPR
(Place to play)

_ _ _ _

ONOM
(Lights up the night)

_ _ _ _

GSIN
(Speak melodiously)

_ _ _ _

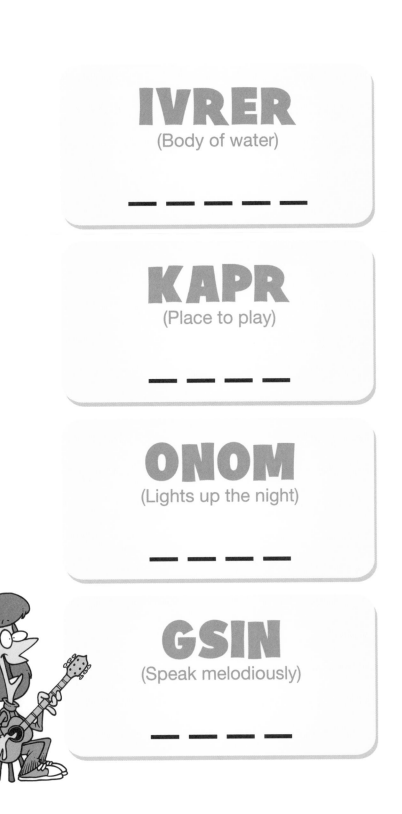

197

What to DO

Find these fun things to do with your family in the word search.
Look up, down, backward, forward, and diagonally.

ARTS AND CRAFTS

BIKE RIDE

BIRD WATCHING

CHARADES

CHECKERS

DANCE

GAME NIGHT

PICNIC

SEE A MOVIE

TOUCH FOOTBALL

```
S D H G T Y U V F R E Q S F E E
L L A B T O O F H C U O T H I B
V I J N T I Y O U V D L G Y V M
F H O O C U G U F C T U N G O J
R A S P Y E B H C F R H I F M U
B C R Y M E T Y C R F F H R A Y
K I E R V F Y T I T V E C D E H
F E K N G A M E N I G H T S E T
H R C E N U G F C O O V A A S G
D I E Q R Y C T I K U H W E R F
U A H E T I D R P I Y R D S T R
R L C R J O D U X U H A R E U E
E K D G T O F E C J R W I D Y D
Q C I J G T B I F A O R B X J S
Z K U Z B R H L H L O W G C V E
R S S T F A R C D N A S T R A D
```

198

Answer on page 280

Out of Order

The story below is listed in the wrong order. Write the numbers of the correct order in the spaces below.

1) "I brought a flashlight!" I said.

2) "Run!" I shouted. And we ran out of the cave.

3) I met my best friend at the park.

4) "Why don't we go explore the big cave?" my friend replied.

5) At the cave we stepped into the darkness.

6) And so we headed off to the big cave.

7) I switched on my flashlight.

8) When we were safely back in the park, we laughed and laughed.

9) Suddenly, hundreds of bats came flying toward us.

10) In the park I asked my friend, "What do want to do today?"

— — — — — — — — — —

199

On the Farm

Use the clues below to complete this crossword puzzle.

ACROSS
2 Says "moo!"
3 Farm equipment you drive
4 Keep the animals in.
6 Ready to ride

DOWN
1 Prepare the field
2 How about some eggs?
5 It all starts with these
6 Bales of food

Answer on page 281

Decode-a-Message

Use the code key below to find a message
that has to do with souvenirs.

A=3	I=14	S=13
D=10	L=4	T=5
E=16	M=11	U=1
F=17	N=15	W=12
G=2	O=6	Y=7
H=8	R=9	

11 6 11   3 15 10   10 3 10

12 16 15 5   5 6   11 3 1 14

3 15 10   3 4 4   14   2 6 5

12 3 13   5 8 14 13

17 1 15 15 7   5 13 8 14 9 5.

201

Word Game

Look at the words and pictures below. Figure out
what detective phrase it means and fill it in the lines below.

Secret ←
Secret!

_ _ _ _ _ _ _ _

Answer on page 281

Picnic Basket

Can you make **25** or more words from the following two words?

PICNIC BASKET

_____   _____
_____   _____
_____   _____
_____   _____
_____   _____
_____   _____
_____   _____
_____   _____
_____   _____
_____   _____
_____   _____
_____   _____

Answer on page 281

Cornfield

Follow the path from **Start** to **Finish** to help
the farmer get through the cornfield.

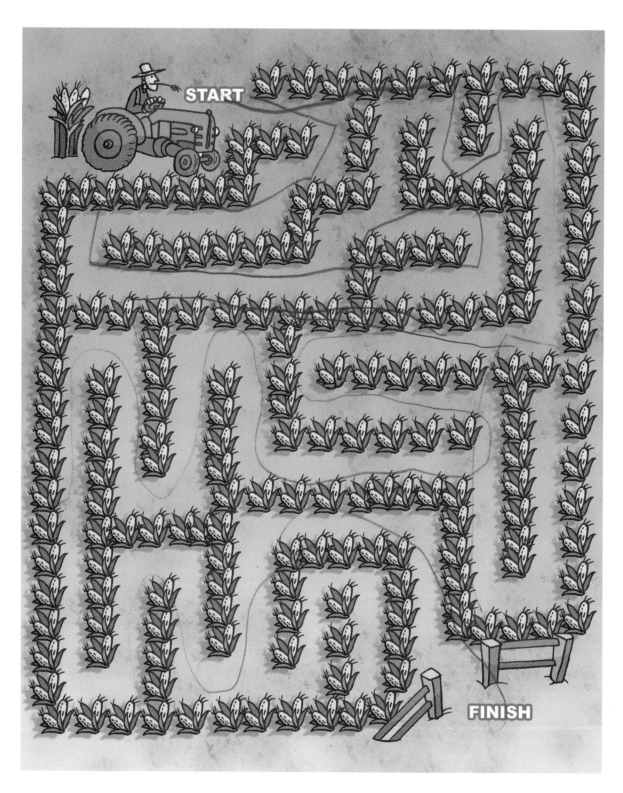

Answer on page 282

In the Garden

Use the pictures below to complete this crossword puzzle.

ACROSS

1 (picture) 5 (picture) 7 (picture) 8 (picture) 10 (picture) 12 (picture)

DOWN

2 (picture) 3 (picture) 4 (picture) 6 (picture) 9 (picture) 11 (picture)

Bird Watching

Solve this rebus puzzle to learn the name of a beautiful, yellow bird often seen at bird feeders.

You are the Poet!

Fill in the last word of each sentence with a word that rhymes to complete the poem.

While walking through the **FOG**,

Out hopped a big, green _____.

I stepped away in **FRIGHT**,

Worried he might _____.

Then I remembered **THIS**,

They don't do that, they _____.

Although it made me **WINCE**.

I made that guy a _____.

Foul Basketball Play

Search, find, and circle these **10** things.

PENGUIN   FIRE HYDRANT   TYPEWRITER
PARKING METER   GAS CAN   CACTUS
HAIR DRYER   ANTEATER   WALRUS
GINGERBREAD MAN

Answer on page 283

Campfire

Find 10 differences between the picture on the top and the one on the bottom.

Answer on page 283

Word Scramble

Unscramble each of these words, using the clues.

CRKO
(A stone, pebble, or boulder)

_ _ _ _

RKEBA
(Smash, destroy)

_ _ _ _ _

LUDBI
(To construct or put together)

_ _ _ _ _

VEERS
(What a waiter does in a restaurant)

_ _ _ _ _

TNSE
(Home for birds)

_ _ _ _

GINS
(Belt out a song)

_ _ _ _

DANS
(It's at the beach)

_ _ _ _

ILAS
(Do this on a boat)

_ _ _ _

210

Autumn

Find these things that have to do with autumn.
Look up, down, backward, forward, and diagonally.

Basket
Sweater
Fireplace
Cider

Donut
Pumpkin
Harvest
Apples

Foliage
Chocolate

```
I  S  W  J  X  V  V  Z  K  J  E  U  N  D  E
I  W  O  K  Z  U  C  W  O  Y  F  F  M  R  Z
X  E  J  Z  T  U  R  S  R  E  F  K  T  W  Q
L  A  F  H  N  K  V  E  C  W  N  E  E  S  F
B  T  P  O  N  T  D  G  P  Q  K  C  G  E  K
T  E  T  Q  J  I  I  Y  D  S  E  H  A  L  Z
P  R  U  W  C  B  K  F  A  I  F  O  I  P  Y
H  C  N  L  O  I  Z  B  X  U  I  C  L  P  W
A  C  O  F  J  A  K  H  F  I  R  O  O  A  Y
R  B  D  M  Z  M  Z  W  U  Q  E  L  F  U  A
V  Z  N  Y  L  Q  Z  X  C  Z  P  A  M  P  V
E  W  J  F  V  J  J  U  C  L  T  U  O  Z
S  A  P  U  M  P  K  I  N  N  A  E  I  P  I
T  G  N  W  Z  F  I  L  D  N  C  J  Q  E  O
K  F  N  H  Z  F  D  Z  E  Z  E  G  M  J  I
```

211

You Complete the Story!

The following story has many blank spaces.
Fill in the spaces using words from the list below
to create your own version of the story.

I was walking along the _____ when I heard a strange noise. It

sounded like a loud _____ . Looking up, I spotted a huge

_____ zooming across the sky. What is that thing, I thought? It looks

like a great big _____ . I ran home to tell my _____ all

about it. When I got home, much to my shock, the _____ I had seen

was sitting in my living room having a cup of _____ with my mom

and dad. This was the strangest day I ever had. Except for that time I went to

the _____ with a twelve-legged _____ !

ROOF · MOUNTAIN · BEACH · ROAD · CHICKEN
APE · COW · BABY · SIREN · SHIP · ROCKET
HOT DOG · BANANA · HEAD · FOOT · SISTER
BROTHER · COUSIN · PET · CHIMP · GOLDFISH · TEA
MILK · COFFEE · BRAINS · CIRCUS · CARNIVAL
PARADE · EGGPLANT · CROCODILE · TEACHER

Answer on page 284

World of Money

Use the clues below to complete this crossword puzzle.

ACROSS
2 England
5 Israel
7 Twenty-five cents
8 Mexico
9 Ten cents

DOWN
1 Russia
3 United States
4 Five cents
6 Europe
8 One cent

Answer on page 284

Decode-a-Message

Use the code key below to find something that lives way up north.

A=5 E=7 O=2 R=4
B=6 L=1 P=3

_3 _2 _1 _5 _4   _6 _7 _5 _4

Answer on page 284

Dinnertime

It's dinnertime for these animals, but their foods are mixed up.
Draw a line from each animal to the correct bowl.

Fun and Games

Can you make **25** or more words
from the following phrase?

FUN AND GAMES

Answer on page 285

Winter Maze

Follow the path from **Start** to **Finish** to help
the polar bear get to the snowman.

FINISH

START

217

Body Language

Use the pictures below to complete this crossword puzzle.

Answer on page 285

Summer Fun

Solve this rebus puzzle to discover a great place for summer fun.

True or False?

Write a **T** next to the true statements and
an **F** next to the false ones.

Jupiter is the largest planet in our solar system. ____

Earth has one moon. ____

Most of Earth is covered by water. ____

Astronauts have walked on the moon. ____

Humans have walked on Mars. ____

Earth is the third planet out from the sun. ____

Answer on page 286

Football

Search, find, and circle these 10 things.

PENCIL
DRUM
BIRD NEST

BONE
SOCCER BALL
SPEAKER
COOKIE

FLOWERPOT
CLOWN
GOLF CLUB

221

Bumper Cars

Find 10 differences between the picture on the top and the one on the bottom.

Answer on page 286

Word Scramble

Unscramble each of these words, using the clues.

DOLEM
(Likes to pose)

_ _ _ _ _

ONGTA
(Dance)

_ _ _ _ _

UGLAU
(Happy sound)

_ _ _ _ _

PEALP
(Fruit)

_ _ _ _ _

CARELL
(Take back)

_ _ _ _ _ _

NGUYO
(Not old)

_ _ _ _ _

223

Answer on page 286

Carnival

Find these things in the word search that have to do with the carnival. Look up, down, backward, forward, and diagonally.

People
Popcorn
Rides
Camera
Prizes

Roller coaster
Ferris Wheel
Bumper cars
Cotton candy
Games

```
M  T  O  B  P  E  L  P  O  E  P  C  F  A  P
Y  Z  R  G  O  Z  Z  G  O  I  O  O  S  U  D
D  G  R  A  A  J  S  E  K  M  C  L  G  F  J
N  E  E  P  D  M  W  A  Q  X  X  A  E  M  M
A  O  T  Q  S  G  E  A  W  F  T  R  B  B  P
C  G  S  J  X  S  D  S  H  M  R  S  U  S  S
N  W  A  G  U  Q  N  Q  C  I  H  W  M  Y  Z
O  T  O  C  Q  K  X  N  S  W  N  S  P  B  P
T  M  C  P  D  A  Y  W  V  R  L  P  E  G  S
T  V  R  J  M  O  H  Z  H  R  V  O  R  C  E
O  J  E  Y  P  E  Y  M  R  W  R  E  C  O  Z
C  X  L  U  E  T  V  M  W  I  Q  Y  A  K  I
N  G  L  L  Z  X  T  X  J  I  D  W  R  F  R
F  U  O  R  C  A  M  E  R  A  E  E  S  P  P
H  H  R  T  O  P  O  P  C  O  R  N  S  W  Z
```

224

new Arrangement

Starting at the arrow, write every fourth letter going around the circle in a clockwise direction, in the spaces below.

___ ___ ___ ___ ___

Answer on page 287

Let's Dance!

Unscramble these ballet terms on the blanks below and then place them in the crossword puzzle.

Answer on page 287

ACROSS

1 ITPOEN

_____

2 ELRANILAB

_____

3 AQEESRABU

_____

4 EEELVR

_____

DOWN

5 RERAB

_____

6 ETEJ

_____

7 RIPETTEUO

_____

8 ILEP

_____

226

Decode-a-Riddle

Write the letter that comes **TWO LETTERS BEFORE** each letter shown below to decode and solve this riddle.

Y J A   Y C U

V J G   D G N V

C T T G U V G F ?

H Q T   J Q N F K P I

W R   V J G   R C P V U

227

Wonder-Ful

Solve this rebus puzzle to discover the name of one of America's most beautiful natural wonders.

Answer on page 288

Secretary

Can you make **15** or more words of
5 or more letters from the following word?

SECRETARY

_____   _____

_____   _____

_____   _____

_____   _____

_____   _____

_____   _____

_____   _____

_____   _____

_____   _____

_____   _____

_____   _____

_____   _____

Answer on page 288

Clock

Follow the path from **Start** to **Finish** to help the mouse go through the clock.

Answer on page 288

What Shape Am I?

Put the shape of each picture in the crossword puzzle below.

Answers

Page 4
What Doesn't Belong?

Group 1
DIRT
SEEDS
FLOWERS
(BUS)
SHOVEL

Group 2
CLOWN
JUGGLER
(BASKETBALL)
ELEPHANT
ACROBAT

Group 3
BALL
BAT
GLOVE
UNIFORM
(FISH)

Group 4
WATER
JUICE
(HOT DOG)
MILK
TEA

Page 5
At the Movies

ACROSS
2 Singing
8 Serious
10 Facing danger
11 Terrorize the audience.

DOWN
1 Real life stuff
2 Scary creature
3 No talking!
4 Lots of laughs
5 Cartoons
6 Magical realms
7 Aboard starships
9 Keep 'em moving.

Crossword answers:
ANIMATION
DOCUMENTARY
FANTASY
MUSICAL
MONSTER
SILENT
COMEDY
SPACE
DRAMA
ACTION
ADVENTURE
HORROR

Page 6
Decode-a-Message

A=5	G=8	K=16	O=14	T=7
C=10	H=4	L=9	R=1	U=2
D=3	I=12	N=6	S=11	W=13
E=17				Y=15

Y O U   C A N ' T
15 14 2   10 5 6 7

T E A C H   A N   O L D
7 17 5 10 4   5 6   14 9 3

D O G   N E W
3 14 8   6 17 13

T R I C K S.
7 1 12 10 16 11

Page 7
Double Dogs

232

Answers

Page 8
Unbelievable

UNBELIEVABLE

Here are just a few:

able	been	eve	nail
ail	bell	even	nub
all	bib	evil	vain
babe	bill	ill	van
bail	bin	lab	veal
ball	blue	lean	veil
ban	bulb	lie	vein
bane	bull	line	via
bean	bun	live	vine
beau	eave	lube	
bee	eel	nab	

Page 9
Strawberry Picking

Page 10
Fun at the Park

Page 11
Carry Away

MESSENGER BAG

Answers

Page 12
Harbor Hunt

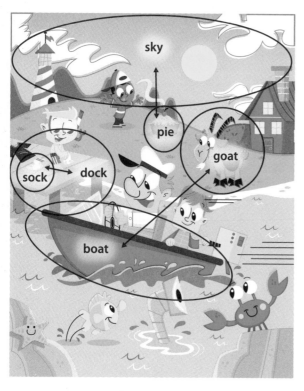

sky

pie

goat

sock → dock

boat

Page 13
A Night at the Movies

Page 14
Fun at the Fair

Page 15
Word Scramble

UKPHNCIM
(Small, cute mammal)

C H I P M U N K

RAPSIEADP
(Vanish)

D I S A P P E A R

PUSTCES
(Imagine, guess)

S U S P E C T

IPRGONPD
(Falling)

D R O P P I N G

NATRAMETP
(Place to live)

A P A R T M E N T

MICRANLI
(Someone who breaks the law)

C R I M I N A L

LCEIVHE
(Car, boat, train)

V E H I C L E

RNSODRUU
(Encase, enclose)

S U R R O U N D

Answers

Page 16
National Parks

Yosemite   Glacier
Yellowstone   Redwood
Acadia   Sequoia
Olympic   Saguaro
Everglades   Shenandoah

Page 17
Unscramble and Fill-In

TAERBT _____ **BATTER**
RMREMDU _____ **DRUMMER**
FSRERU _____ **SURFER**
REAGND _____ **GARDEN**
ISTIPR _____ **SPIRIT**

When starting a __GARDEN__ , you need lots of rich soil.

The __BATTER__ hit a long home run to deep right field.

The __SURFER__ got very excited seeing the enormous waves in the ocean.

The ghost hunter captured evidence of a __SPIRIT__ with her electronic equipment.

The __DRUMMER__ in the band played a long, loud solo.

Page 18
Communicating

across
3 Typing with your thumbs
4 Put this in a mailbox.
6 Call me up.
8 Through the machine, over the wires
10 A chat

DOWN
1 Dots and dashes
2 Call from anywhere.
5 Watch your favorite TV show.
7 Tune it in and listen.
9 Computer message

Page 19
Decode-a-Riddle

!=A	*=H	>=O	?=V
@=B	(=I	[=P	/=W
#=C	+=J	]=Q	\=X
$=D	)=K	"=R	}=Y
%=E	;=L	"=S	{=Z
^=F	:=M	'=T	
&=G	<=N	'=U	

W H A T   D I D   T H E
H O U S E   W E A R ?

A D D R E S S

235

Answers

Page 20
Word Game

HEAD
HEALS

H E A D   O V E R
H E E L S

Page 21
Beautiful

BEAUTIFUL

Here are just a few:

able	eat	flea	tab
ate	elf	flu	tail
bait	fail	fuel	tale
bat	fat	lab	tea
beat	fate	late	teal
belt	felt	leaf	tie
bet	fib	left	tile
bit	file	let	tub
bite	fit	lie	tuba
blue	flab	life	tube
but	flat	lift	

Page 22
Circus Maze

Page 23
Extreme Sports

Answers

Page 24
All Mixed Up

 + + = ICE-CREAM SUNDAE

 + + = PEANUT BUTTER SANDWICH

 + + = CHRISTMAS TREE STAND

 + +  = BALLPOINT PEN

Page 25
House Call

Page 26
Snowball Fight

Page 27
The Big Apple

Answers

Page 28
Word Scramble

IRLAONIG
(Unique)
O R I G I N A L

RUTENA
(The great outdoors)
N A T U R E

RAFORDW
(Moving ahead)
F O R W A R D

SBENRUM
(Count with these)
N U M B E R S

KCEJTA
(Coat)
J A C K E T

TARPREN
(Teammate)
P A R T N E R

NOEBLG
(Connected to)
B E L O N G

ANEOSS
(Time of year)
S E A S O N

Page 29
Backyard Games

Hide and seek   Baseball
Kickball   Football
Volleyball   Badminton
Bocce   Horseshoes
Tag   Croquet

Page 30
Vowel Maze

W	R	E	T	L	P
A	S	F	G	H	J
K	L	Z	V	U	N
M	Q	W	R	T	I
S	U	F	N	P	M
W	J	O	F	E	K

B E A U T I F U L   H O R S E

Page 31
Brr, Cold!

ACROSS	DOWN
1 Feet	1 Neck
2 Head	3 Hands

Crossword:
³M
 I
 T
¹S L I P P E R S
 C   T
²H A T E
 A   N
 R   S
 F
MITTENS / SLIPPERS / SCARF / HAT

Answers

Page 32
Decode-a-Riddle

! = A	° = H	> = O	? = V
@ = B	(= I	[= P	/ = W
# = C	+ = J	] = Q	\ = X
$ = D	) = K	" = R	} = Y
% = E	; = L	" = S	{ = Z
^ = F	: = M	' = T	
& = G	< = N	' = U	

W H A T K I N D O F
F L O W E R D O E S
E V E R Y O N E
H A V E?

T W O L I P S

Page 33
Double Boats

Page 34
Situational

SITUATIONAL

Here are just a few:

alas	list	sail	sun
also	lit	salt	tail
alto	loan	sat	tan
ant	lost	sit	tilt
aunt	lots	slit	tin
auto	nail	slot	tint
into	not	soil	toil
its	nut	son	ton
last	oat	soul	tot
lint	oil	stun	tuna
lion	out	suit	unit

Page 35
Ferris Wheel

START   FINISH

Answers

Page 36
Relationships

Page 37
On the Road

T A X I C A B
M E T E R

Page 38
Going to the City

Page 39
The Pet Shop

Answers

Page 40
Skating Fun

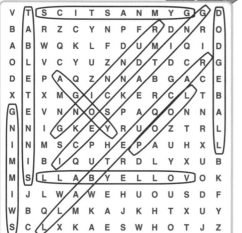

Page 41
Word Scramble

NEFDIR
(Buddy, pal)

F R I E N D

AELNCRE
(Fresher, not dirty)

C L E A N E R

IPNOTRO
(Part, piece)

P O R T I O N

EWOHRS
(Sprinkle)

S H O W E R

LITSEHO
(Not friendly)

H O S T I L E

ENDCOS
(Not first)

S E C O N D

TKAACT
(Assault)

A T T A C K

ITRNAUC
(Drape)

C U R T A I N

Page 42
Indoor Sports

VOLLEYBALL   GYMNASTICS
DODGEBALL   TABLE TENNIS
RACQUETBALL   POOL
SWIMMING   YOGA
RUNNING
ICE SKATING

Page 43
Haunted House

Answers

Page 44
Where's the Party?

ACROSS
1 NVREIANRYAS — ANNIVERSARY
2 PTMSIBA — BAPTISM
3 TEWES XSIEETN — SWEET SIXTEEN
4 RAB TVHMIAZ — BAR MITZVAH

DOWN
5 DWEDGIN — WEDDING
6 TRHDBIYA — BIRTHDAY
7 DUATAGNROI — GRADUATION
8 MERETIERTN — RETIREMENT

Crossword answers:
1 ANNIVERSARY
2 BAPTISM
3 SWEETSIXTEEN
4 BARMITZVAH
5 WEDDING
6 BIRTHDAY
7 GRADUATION
8 RETIREMENT

Page 45
Decode-a-Riddle

IF YOU PUT A BLUE HAT INTO THE RED SEA WHAT DOES IT BECOME?

WET

Page 46
Double Squirrels

Page 47
Flabbergasted

FLABBERGASTED

Here are just a few:

after	blast	federal	related
agreed	bread	flags	safer
alert	dabble	fleas	salad
algebra	darts	garbled	salted
altered	deals	gates	sealed
atlas	dearest	glade	sleet
badge	debater	grabbed	stable
badger	defeat	grated	staged
bagel	desert	greased	stare
barge	eager	great	steed
beagle	eagle	large	table
bearable	eater	later	teased
beard	erase	least	trade
beast	fable	rafts	trees
beatable	false	readable	
beret	faster	rebate	
blade	feast	rebels	

242

Answers

Page 48
Robot Maze

Page 49
What does Baby Need?

Page 50
Telecom

Page 51
Into the Forest

Answers

Page 52
Outer Space

Page 53
Back to School

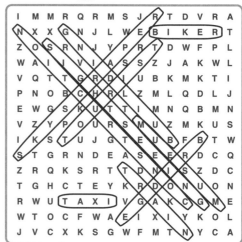

Page 54
Word Scramble

DINECMIE
(Makes you better)

M E D I C I N E

RHETCEA
(Learning professional)

T E A C H E R

SMTASTRE
(Where one sleeps)

M A T T R E S S

NSTREMO
(Scary creature)

M O N S T E R

KMKESILHA
(Ice-cream drink)

M I L K S H A K E

RERPNPASW
(Printed current events)

N E W S P A P E R

DYWBRAOA
(Where plays are performed)

B R O A D W A Y

MEILACMORC
(Sells ads)

C O M M E R C I A L

Page 55
In the City

Skyscraper   Tourist
Bridge   Biker
Building   Museum
Taxi   Sightseeing
Construction Train

244

Answers

Page 56
Odd Stuff

A	B	C	D	E	F	G	H	I	J	K	L	M
N	O	P	Q	R	S	T	U	V	W	X	Y	Z

U I F S F
J T
B
G M Z
J O
N Z
T P V Q

<u>T</u> <u>H</u> <u>E</u> <u>R</u> <u>E</u>   <u>I</u> <u>S</u>   <u>A</u>

<u>F</u> <u>L</u> <u>Y</u>   <u>I</u> <u>N</u>   <u>M</u> <u>Y</u>   <u>S</u> <u>O</u> <u>U</u> <u>P</u>!

Page 57
It's all Relative

across
3 Second ____, once removed
6 Child of one's child
9 Your parent's sister
10 Female sibling
11 Female parent
12 Your mother's mother

DOWN
1 Male sibling
2 Male child
4 Your father's father
5 Your parent's brother
7 Female child
8 Male parent

Page 58
Decode-a-Message

A=6	F=1	M=2	P=5	T=10
C=9	I=4	N=14	R=7	U=13
E=12	L=8	O=11	S=3	

<u>A</u> <u>L</u> <u>I</u> <u>E</u> <u>N</u> <u>S</u>   <u>F</u> <u>R</u> <u>O</u> <u>M</u>
6 8 4 12 14 3   1 7 11 2

<u>O</u> <u>U</u> <u>T</u> <u>E</u> <u>R</u>   <u>S</u> <u>P</u> <u>A</u> <u>C</u> <u>E</u>
11 13 10 12 7   3 5 6 9 12

Page 59
Which is Witch?

Answers

Page 60
Encyclopedia

ENCYCLOPEDIA

Here are just a few:

alien	cyclone	leaned	pedal
alone	cynical	lined	pelican
alpine	daily	loaned	pencil
cancel	dance	nailed	piano
candle	decal	nicely	piece
candy	decay	niece	piled
caned	decline	ocean	place
canoe	decoy	oiled	placid
canopy	deeply	oldie	plaid
caped	delay	opened	plain
clean	delicacy	openly	plane
cloned	denial	paced	played
code	elope	pained	police
coined	encode	panel	policy
conceal	eyelid	panic	yelped
coped	ideal	peace	yield
copied	laced	pealed	yodel
cycle	lacey	pecan	

Page 61
Tree House

Page 62
Face the Music

Page 63
Inside Room

- BULB +

- M - MER +

- A - XI +

- OCO - LATE

L I G H T S W I T C H

Answers

Page 64
Zoo Mania

wheel
seal
bear
pear
hat
bat
ZOO

Page 65
Playground

Page 66
Life on Mars

Page 67
Word Scramble

SYEA
(Simple to do)

E A S Y

AEKC
(With frosting)

C A K E

ERDA
(Do this with a book)

R E A D

YAPL
(Enjoy a game)

P L A Y

ONRH
(Beep! beep! in a car)

H O R N

SAERE
(Rub out)

E R A S E

KATCR
(A train runs on this)

T R A C K

DISBR
(They fly in the sky)

B I R D S

Answers

Page 68
Weddings

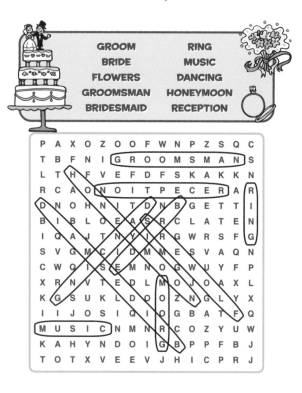

GROOM   RING
BRIDE   MUSIC
FLOWERS   DANCING
GROOMSMAN   HONEYMOON
BRIDESMAID   RECEPTION

Page 69
Odd Maze

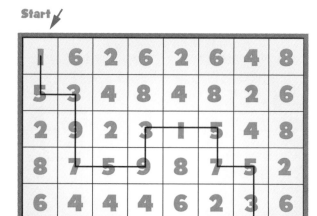

Start

1	6	2	6	2	6	4	8
5	3	4	8	4	8	2	6
2	9	2	3	1	5	4	8
8	7	5	9	8	7	5	2
6	4	4	4	6	2	3	6
2	4	6	2	6	8	7	2
8	6	8	4	6	2	9	3
2	8	8	6	4	6	4	7

Finish

Page 70
Musical Types

ACROSS
1 Singers perform
6 Music only, no voices
8 ___ and roll
9 Classical singers
10 From all over the globe

DOWN
2 Symphony orchestra
3 Acousitc guitar with lyrics
4 ___-hop
5 Mix of rock and jazz
7 Swings

Crossword solution:
1 VOCAL
2 CLASSICAL
3 FOLK
4 HIP
5 FUSION
6 INSTRUMENTAL
7 JAZZ
8 ROCK
9 OPERA
10 WORLD

Page 71
Decode-a-Riddle

1=A	8=H	15=O	22=V
2=B	9=I	16=P	23=W
3=C	10=J	17=Q	24=X
4=D	11=K	18=R	25=Y
5=E	12=L	19=S	26=Z
6=F	13=M	20=T	
7=G	14=N	21=U	

W H A T   G O E S   U P
23 8 1 20   7 15 5 19   21 16

B U T   N E V E R
2 21 20   14 5 22 5 18

C O M E S   D O W N?
3 15 13 5 19   4 15 23 14

Y O U R   A G E
25 15 21 18   1 7 5

Answers

Page 72
Double Digits

Page 73
Theatrical

 THEATRICAL

Here are just a few:

ace	cat	hit	rice
ache	chat	ice	rich
acre	each	itch	tact
act	ear	lace	tail
ail	eat	lair	tale
air	era	late	tar
ale	etch	let	tart
arc	hail	liar	tea
arch	hair	lice	tear
are	hat	lie	that
area	hate	lit	the
art	heal	race	tic
ate	hear	rail	tie
car	heat	rat	tile
care	her	rate	tilt
cart	hire	real	tire

Page 74
Baseball Maze

Page 75
Things That Go!

```
¹T R U C K
R         ²H
³A I R P L A N E      ⁴A
I         N          U
N         G      ⁵T  T
      ⁶B  G      R  O
      U   L      O  M
⁷J E T S K I     L  O
      D   E      L  B
      E         ⁸B O A T
⁹M O T O R C Y C L E  I
                   E  L
                      E
```

Answers

Page 76
Sweet Treat

🐭🐭 - M

🐱 - A - T + R +

👂 - R + M

$$\underline{I} \ \underline{C} \ \underline{E}$$
$$\underline{C} \ \underline{R} \ \underline{E} \ \underline{A} \ \underline{M}$$

Page 77
Matching Rhymes

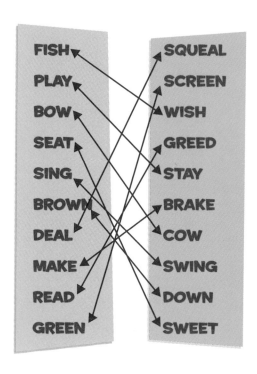

FISH → WISH
PLAY → STAY
BOW → COW
SEAT → SWEET
SING → SCREEN
BROWN → DOWN
DEAL → SQUEAL
MAKE → BRAKE
READ → GREED
GREEN → SWING

Page 78
Butterfly Beauties

Page 79
Food Fight!

Answers

Page 80
Word Scramble

FITNEYID
(To name or recognize)

I D E N T I F Y

SEATDINC
(A far way to go)

D I S T A N C E

CHEARSER
(Look up)

R E S E A R C H

DOTRUCCNO
(Leader of a train or orchestra)

C O N D U C T O R

VIMCOREAW
(Oven for fast cooking)

M I C R O W A V E

NITLARBIL
(Bright, very smart)

B R I L L I A N T

CITEURODN
(Meet, start)

I N T R O D U C E

RAPTOPOHGH
(Picture)

P H O T O G R A P H

Page 81
Well-Known Authors

Hemingway
Cummings
Dickinson
Anderson
Alcott

Carroll
Hitchcock
London
Shakespeare
Whitman

```
R D H F V M O W G U O R X I C Y P W V X
G P S S C O T Y D Q Q O O P K S F V P G
S B Q G H E D H L T H K O B J O M M M L
P U K J E A U W R Z I Q W G J P N O Y W
O J R C Q Z K N I H Z E V U E N H Q O T
F O R U K P F E F M W I P N K O E L V F
N O P Y A K W G S M D P R J C U M P L P
Y Y L L N S M L Q P Z D T G O S I N P A X
L B C A R R O L L E N F W C V H J X F
H L T L M O J N M O A U R H A G D C B
J G T B K C S D N M N R O C A F W L Q I
Q S Z I E Y N D T A E D E T F I V Y C S
U D U O R V U I I W R E O S I V C D I
C G Q P X C H U O E S Y Z N H N B G D C
F Z N T O W C L O R Q F T J F K N V A K
R L B B S D R P F Q T W X X I I Z W I
Q Q B G S K V I B A V B R J M D J R O N
G D N N O S R E D N A I A M I D D R E S
O T A Z D R G G D B Y I U X I J X T S O N
G H G T T O C L A A D C S X E F Y E F
```

Page 82
Word Chains

Flowers:

DAFFODIL, L <u>ILAC</u> , <u>CARNATION</u>

Musical Instruments:

HARP, P <u>IANO</u> , <u>OBOE</u>

Holidays:

HALLOWEEN, N <u>EW YEAR'S EVE</u> , <u>EASTER</u>

Clothing:

HAT, T <u>ROUSERS</u> , <u>SCARF</u>

U.S. Cities:

HOUSTON, N <u>EW YORK</u> , <u>KANSAS CITY</u>

Page 83
Cryptids—Do They Exist?

ACROSS
2 Mysterious Native American creature
4 Single horned horse
8 Creature from Garden State
10 Himalayan bigfoot
11 Aliens with big eyes, round heads
12 Frozen creature of stories

DOWN
1 Lake monster of Scotland
3 Mexican creature of legend
5 Creature who swims in Lake Champlain
6 Sea creature with tentacles
7 Half-fish, half-female human
9 Man-ape of the woods

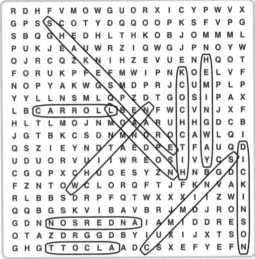

Across/Down solution grid:
- 1 DOWN: LOCHNESSMONSTER
- 2 ACROSS: SASQUATCH
- 4 ACROSS: UNICORN
- 3 DOWN: CHUPACABRA
- 5 DOWN: CHAMP
- 6 DOWN: GIANTSQUID
- 7 DOWN: MERMAID
- 8 ACROSS: JERSEYDEVIL
- 9 DOWN: BIGFOOT
- 10 ACROSS: YETI
- 11 ACROSS: GREYS
- 12 ACROSS: ABOMINABLESNOWMAN

Answers

Page 84
Decode-a-Message

E=2   O=6   T=9
I=4   R=1   V=3
N=5   S=8   W=7

I T ' S   N O W   O R
4 9 8   5 6 7   6 1

N E V E R .
5 2 3 2 1

Page 85
Word Game

J A C K   I N
T H E   B O X

Page 86
Pictures and Words

B E L L   C A N D L E   F I N G E R

able	blend	deal	feline	label
acre	blind	declare	fence	land
aged	brain	degree	fern	lead
agile	bread	dial	field	leaf
agreed	bride	dinner	final	lean
alien	cabin	drag	fine	life
angel	cable	drain	fire	linen
badge	cage	eager	flag	nail
bagel	calf	eagle	flea	near
bald	calling	edge	fleece	nice
ball	candle	elder	fling	racing
band	cane	elegance	fried	rain
barn	card	ending	gain	read
bead	cell	engineer	garden	real
bear	cellar	enlarge	garlic	recall
beard	cider	fable	gear	recline
beef	clean	fabric	gerbil	reef
been	clear	face	glad	refill
begin	crab	failed	glide	regal
bell	cradle	fair	grain	reliable
bill	crib	fallen	green	rice
bird	cried	fear	grid	ride
birdcage	dancer	feed	grill	ring
bland	deaf	feeling	iceberg	

Page 87
Surfing Away

Answers

Page 88
All Sports

Page 89
Rebus Riddle Riot

N +

– L + –

$$\underline{N}\ \underline{I}\ \underline{C}\ \underline{E}$$
$$\underline{B}\ \underline{E}\ \underline{L}\ \underline{T}$$

Page 90
Going Fishing

Page 91
Shopping Spree

Answers

Page 92
Take Off!

Page 93
Word Scramble

SOCIPT
(Subjects)

T O P I C S

EMLPOTEC
(Finished, all done)

C O M P L E T E

UTSSAT
(Situation, condition)

S T A T U S

ETCKTI
(Gets you into an event)

T I C K E T

NIETONS
(Stress, pressure)

T E N S I O N

RUELUCT
(Music, art, dance)

C U L T U R E

LGTURESG
(Difficult time)

S T R U G G L E

PLEHED
(Assisted)

H E L P E D

Page 94
Garden

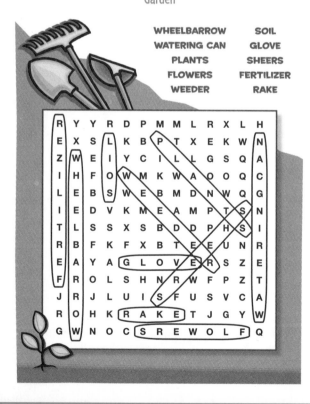

WHEELBARROW   SOIL
WATERING CAN   GLOVE
PLANTS   SHEERS
FLOWERS   FERTILIZER
WEEDER   RAKE

Page 95
Figure Out the Phrases

 + = UP AND RUNNING

 + = IN AND OUT

 + = BACK AND FORTH

 + = SHORT AND SWEET

Answers

Page 96

How are You Feeling?

Page 96

across
1 Feeling great
3 I need to cool off.
4 Let's eat!
6 Thrilled
7 Ready for a nap

DOWN
2 I'm so mad!
3 Anxious
5 A bit blue

Crossword:
¹H ²A P P Y
  N
  G
  ³W A R M
  O R Y
⁴H U N G R Y ⁵S
  R   A
⁶E X C I T E D
  E
⁷T I R E D

Page 97

Decode-a-Riddle

WHAT HAPPENED
T E X Q   E X M M B K B A

WHEN THE
T E B K   Q E B

VAMPIRE GOT
S X J M F O B   D L Q

CAUGHT IN
Z X R D E Q   F K

A SNOWSTORM?
X   P K L T P Q L O J

HE GOT
E B   D L Q

FROSTBITE.
C O L P Q Y F Q B

Page 98

Double Bedroom

Page 99

Bottomless

BOTTOMLESS

Here are just a few:

belts	bottle	moles	solos
bless	bottom	moose	stems
bloom	emboss	motel	stole
blossom	looms	motto	stool
bolts	loose	oboes	tests
booms	loses	slobs	tombs
boost	loots	slots	tools
bootless	lotto	smelt	totem
boots	melts	soles	

Answers

Page 100
Train Maze

Page 101
Lights! Camera! Action!

Page 102
"Arr"-Great-Rebus

Page 103
Treasure Hunt

Answers

Page 104
Grocery Store

Page 105
Bake a Cake!

Page 106
Word Scramble

NILOVI
(Instrument)

V I O L I N

VACENR
(Found underground)

C A V E R N

RCADS
(Game)

C A R D S

RFNCEA
(Country)

F R A N C E

TLTBOE
(Drink receptacle)

B O T T L E

PANA
(Town in California)

N A P A

Page 107
Doctor's Visit

Thermometer   Stethoscope
Scale   Depressor
Medicine   Bandage
Nurse   Lollipop
Immunization   Exam

```
V E H P O C H Z H H O F B T T A V M S W
A E P C I R X O Y U U B C A H N M U O Z
Q S A I V N R I C B W G R N L N M L A A
Q R B E Q A Q H B C V H K X C D B D X C
A U W J P B W N H E G M A G M G A A E D
O N Z S E Y H G Z E S P E M C A H G W E
Z R E T E M O M R E H T G D L B O F E P
U X T P L L V Q C R K I H X I S E S W R
A G Y Q J H B W S I J M I H P C B B Z E
T P Y N E W O O J O F M G X U N I H A S
S T E T H O S C O P E U P N K V P N K S
S A L W A K E L L B E N F L G N D U E O
P D I Q B U B H Y O Y I H G B Z E F Z R
A Y Z Q X Q S X T U B Z K I H C M H Y M
M L O L L I P O P A G A L J L D H A B Z
X M N O P G J P V H D T X E S K U Y Z M
J A E L A C S V K A D I C J E G F D A K
R X H W H J X B J Y S O F Z S G S R S G
S E Z B M O E C W O B N Z I C Y N R D Z
Z L Z H Y W M V W Y X W V B W A F A E J
```

Answers

Page 108
Ping-Pong Mix-Up

The other player wins!

Two people decide to play ping pong.

One player misses a shot.

2
6
4
5
3
1

They pick up the paddles.

They play ping pong.

One person points to a ping pong table.

Page 109
Around the World

ACROSS
1 Gnocchi
2 Sushi
3 Enchilada

DOWN
4 Moo shu
5 Jerk chicken
6 Tandoori Chicken
7 Coq au vin
8 Ropa vieja

Page 110
Decode-a-Riddle

WHAT CAN GO
AROUND THE
WORLD WHILE
STAYING ON
THE CORNER?

A STAMP

Page 111
Double Smiles

258

Answers

Page 112
Skywriting

SKYWRITING

Here are just a few:

gist	knits	skirt	twin
grin	rigs	skit	twins
grins	ring	sting	tying
grit	rings	stingy	wigs
grits	rink	stir	wing
inks	rinks	striking	wings
inky	rising	string	winks
iris	risk	stringy	wins
king	risking	swig	wintry
kings	risky	swing	wiring
kiting	sign	tins	wiry
kits	sing	tiny	wits
kiwi	sink	trying	wring
kiwis	skiing	twig	wrist
knit	skin	twigs	writing

Page 113
Picnic Maze

Page 114
Winter Wonderland

Page 115
Snack Time

POPCORN KERNEL

Answers

Page 116
Car Race

Page 117
City Living

Page 118
Poolside Fun

Page 119
Word Scramble

LDMAANITA
(Spotty dog)

D A L M A T I A N

RCEMUYR
(Planet)

M E R C U R Y

MRCAEP
(Outdoor recreationalist)

C A M P E R

NABAAN
(Fruit)

B A N A N A

THEBORRS
(Familial males)

B R O T H E R S

YNORCA
(Drawing instrument)

C R A Y O N

SOSNSAE
(Weather changes)

S E A S O N S

DITNERESP
(In charge)

P R E S I D E N T

Answers

Page 120
Types of Dinosaurs

Archaeopteryx
Allosaurus
Cretaceous
Utahraptor
Stegosaurus
Apatosaurus
Triceratops
Deinonychus
Parasaurolophus
Tyrannosaurus
Oviraptor

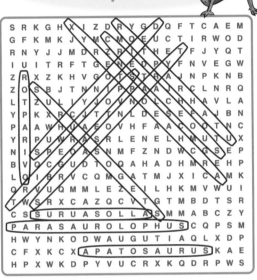

Page 121
Double Words

Type of joke <u>KNOCK</u> - <u>KNOCK</u>

Toy that goes up and down <u>YO</u> - <u>YO</u>

Ballerina's skirt <u>TU</u> - <u>TU</u>

Baby expression for cut or bruise <u>BOO</u> - <u>BOO</u>

Not great, not bad <u>SO</u> - <u>SO</u>

To go wild about something <u>GA</u> - <u>GA</u>

Page 122
World Capitals

across	Down
5 Italy	1 France
7 Belgium	2 Germany
8 Ireland	3 United States
9 Austria	4 Greece
10 Egypt	6 Spain
11 United Kingdom	
12 India	

Page 123
Decode-a-Riddle

W H A T   Q U E S T I O N
Y J C V   S W G U V K Q P

C A N   Y O U   N E V E R
E C P   A Q W   P G X G T

A N S W E R   B Y
C P U Y G T   D A

S A Y I N G "Y E S"?
U C A K P I   A G U

"A R E   Y O U
 C T G   A Q W

A S L E E P?"
C U N G G R

Answers

Page 124
Monumental

  − S − E + O +

7 − N +   − B − E

R O O S E V E L T

Page 125
Noteworthy

NOTEWORTHY

Here are just a few:

eon	now	they	went
hen	one	toe	wet
her	onto	ton	when
hew	ore	tone	whet
hey	owe	too	who
hoe	own	toot	why
hone	rent	tore	woe
hoot	root	torn	won
horn	rot	tot	wont
hot	row	tote	woo
how	rye	tow	wore
net	ten	town	worn
new	tent	toy	wren
nor	tern	trot	yen
not	the	try	yet
note	then	two	yore

Page 126
Motorcycle Derby

Page 127
Let's Go to the Beach

262

Answers

Page 128
Water Rebus

HOUSEBOAT

Page 129
Picture Rhymes

COLUMN 1   COLUMN 2

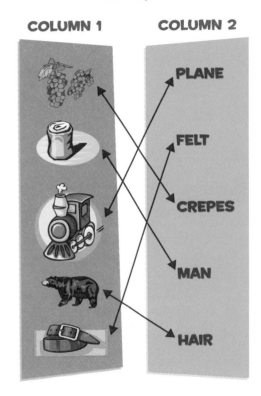

PLANE

FELT

CREPES

MAN

HAIR

Page 130
Swimming Fun

Page 131
Ready, Set, Go!

Answers

Page 132
Word Scramble

HEPAC
(Fruit)

P E A C H

LSAAS
(Spicy sauce)

S A L S A

EPLTA
(Eat off)

P L A T E

OMRES
(Code)

M O R S E

NYNAN
(Kid watcher)

N A N N Y

EDATR
(Swap)

T R A D E

Page 133
Golf

Club
Wood
Swing
Course
Ball

Par
Score
Green
Birdie
Iron

```
F R P X A E K O C P K G G
D F J C E L X W O W A P J
L S T E S W N R U N C R B
A K Z L L A B K R P A X G
I P L A N V J V S I M C C
F A Y E B Q W W E N T K O
V C E U N H W O F O I S S
D R L E B O Z L U J J O C
G C L W O I I R O N B X O
M F V D V R R B X G A R E
C O G C E M A D S E H N
B C R P W X C B I P J G C
T J L S W I N G G E B H Y
```

Page 134
Soup Time!

G E T   I T
W H I L E
I T ' S   H O T !

Page 135
Animal Sounds

ACROSS	DOWN
1 Cat	3 Horse
2 Bird	4 Pig

```
    ³N
¹M E O W
    I
    G   ⁴O
²C H I R P
    N
    K
```

Answers

Page 136
Decode-a-Message

A=2   G=5   N=7   U=6
E=4   L=3   S=1

S	U	N	G	L	A	S	S	E	S
1	6	7	5	3	2	1	1	4	1

Page 137
Under the Sea

Page 138
Particular

PARTICULAR

Here are just a few:

actual	clap	pail	tail
altar	clip	pair	talc
apart	culprit	part	tarp
aria	cult	partial	tiara
aura	curl	pat	tip
aural	curt	pita	trail
cap	cut	purr	trap
capital	lair	rail	trial
carp	lap	rapt	trip
carpal	liar	rat	tulip
cart	lit	ritual	ultra
cat	pact	rural	

Page 139
Penguin Pushover

Answers

Page 140
Party Time

Crossword:
- 1 (down) C
- 2 (down) I
- 3 (across) HAT / (down) CAKE
- 4 (down) GIRL
- 5 (across) ICECREAM / ICICLE
- 6 (down) BABY
- 7 (across) BALLOON
- 8 (across) PRESENT

Page 141
Football Fun

Q + ↑ - P + ♥ - H - E +
🚰 + C + H - ⌚
❄ - WAT + 🏖(BEACH) - CH

QUARTERBACK
SNEAK

Page 142
Wedding Fun

star
chapel
apple
broom
groom
car — JUST MARRIED

Page 143
Flower Shop

Answers

Page 144
Construction Zone

Page 145
Word Scramble

ITPSLAOH
(Place where sick people go)
H O S P I T A L

ALGNIBZ
(On fire)
B L A Z I N G

RULANTA
(From the Earth)
N A T U R A L

FAITACRR
(Plane, jet, helicopter)
A I R C R A F T

TORNGEENAI
(Grandparent, parent, child)
G E N E R A T I O N

AMNOFIITORN
(Facts, knowledge)
I N F O R M A T I O N

ICLVANAR
(Rides, games, cotton candy)
C A R N I V A L

FSAERRTN
(Move, change, shift)
T R A N S F E R

Page 146
School Supplies

Ruler	Calculator
Notebook	Backpack
Compass	Eraser
Pencil	Binder
Protractor	Marker

Page 147
Basketball Mix-Up

The game is over!

A basketball player misses the basket.

There are 3 seconds left in the game!

3
4
6
5
2
1

A basketball player runs down the court.

A basketball player shoots the ball.

There are 2 seconds left in the game!

Answers

Page 148
You were Saying

ACROSS
1 Grizzly **BEARS**
2 Help **WANTED**
3 License to **DRIVE**
4 **SWIM** in the shallow end.

DOWN
2 Wash and **WEAR**
3 Park closes at **DUSK**
5 **READY** or not
6 Seashells on the **SHORE**

Page 149
Decode-a-Riddle

WHAT IS IT
YOU CAN CATCH
BUT YOU CAN'T
THROW?

A COLD

Page 150
Double Cats

Page 151
Frustration

FRUSTRATION

Here are just a few:

ants	fusion	riot	start	tout
artist	info	riots	station	train
arts	insofar	roar	stint	trait
aunt	into	roars	stir	traitor
aunts	intro	roast	stout	transit
auto	ions	rots	strain	trio
autos	iron	ruin	strut	trios
faint	irons	ruins	stun	trot
fair	nitrous	runs	stunt	trots
fairs	nuts	runt	suit	trout
fans	oafs	runts	suitor	trust
fast	oars	rust	surf	tuft
faun	oats	ruts	tarot	tuna
fins	onus	saint	tart	tunas
first	ours	satin	tarts	turf
fist	outfit	sift	taunt	turn
fits	outran	sitar	tins	turns
foist	outs	snit	tint	tutor
font	rafts	snort	tints	unfair
fort	rain	snout	titans	unfit
forts	rainout	soar	toast	unit
fount	rains	sofa	tofu	units
four	rant	soft	tons	unto
fours	ratio	sort	torn	urns
front	ration	sour	tots	
frost	rats	stain	tour	
fruit	rift	stair	tourist	
furs	rifts	star	tours	

Answers

Page 152
Fish Maze

Page 153
Good Sports

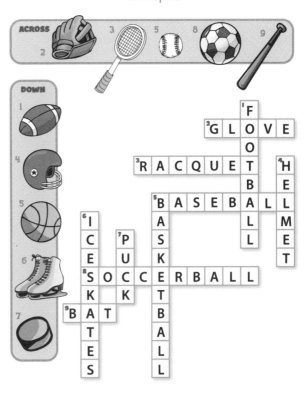

Page 154
Career

B U S I N E S S
S U I T

Page 155
Carnival Night

Answers

Page 156
Happy Birthday to You!

Page 157
Getting Married

Page 158
Word Scramble

SNATRERG
(Person who doesn't know someone)

S T R A N G E R

AVEBHE
(Act properly)

B E H A V E

OCTORES
(Motorized bike)

S C O O T E R

NINRUGN
(Moving very fast)

R U N N I N G

LOHSACEE
(Tie this)

S H O E L A C E

NUSHESIN
(Brightens the day)

S U N S H I N E

ARPDEA
(March in this)

P A R A D E

PILREPYS
(Smooth, icy)

S L I P P E R Y

Page 159
Weather

Humidity
Temperature
Lightning

Tornado
Thunderstorm
Overcast
Doppler

Drizzle
Thermometer
Rainfall

Answers

Page 160
Every Other Letter

B T A R T U H N I K N S G

<u>B</u> <u>A</u> <u>T</u> <u>H</u> <u>I</u> <u>N</u> <u>G</u>   <u>T</u> <u>R</u> <u>U</u> <u>N</u> <u>K</u> <u>S</u>

Page 161
Magic

ACROSS
3 Has one horn
6 Tiny, flying creature
7 Hero with sword and armor
8 Magic charm or curse

DOWN
1 Person of magic
2 Fire-breathing reptile
4 Where the king lives
5 Ugly creature who lives under bridges

Crossword answers:
- W I Z A R D (1 Down)
- D R A G O N (2 Down)
- ³UNICORN (3 Across)
- ⁴CASTLE (4 Down)
- ⁵TROLL (5 Down)
- ⁶FAIRY (6 Across)
- ⁷KNIGHT (7 Across)
- ⁸SPELL (8 Across)

Page 162
Decode-a-Riddle

!=A	*=H	>=O	?=V
@=B	(=I	[=P	/=W
#=C	+=J	]=Q	\=X
$=D	)=K	"=R	}=Y
%=E	;=L	"=S	{=Z
^=F	:=M	'=T	
&=G	<=N	'=U	

<u>A T</u>   <u>W H A T</u>   <u>T I M E</u>
<u>S H O U L D</u>   <u>Y O U</u>
<u>G O</u>   <u>T O</u>   <u>T H E</u>
<u>D E N T I S T</u>?

<u>T O O T H</u>   <u>H U R T Y</u>

Page 163
Word Game

Please

<u>P R E T T Y</u>   <u>P L E A S E</u>
<u>W I T H</u>   <u>A</u>   <u>C H E R R Y</u>
<u>O N</u>   <u>T O P</u>.

Answers

Page 164
Quarantine

QUARANTINE

Here are just a few:

anti	irate	rein	tine
antique	nature	rent	tire
aqua	near	retain	train
area	neat	retina	true
arena	nine	rite	tuna
aria	quaint	ruin	tune
aunt	quart	rune	tuner
aura	quiet	runt	turn
earn	quit	tanner	unit
inert	quite	tear	unite
innate	rain	tern	untie
inner	rant	tiara	
intern	rate	tier	

Page 165
Bear Ice Maze

Page 166
Music to Your Ears

Page 167
Sweet Stuff

CANDY CANE

272

Answers

Page 168
School's Cool!

Page 169
Pumpkins

Page 170
Dinosaur Duo

Page 171
Word Scramble

IBGERD
(Takes you over water)

B R I D G E

RTSGNI
(Tie stuff up with this)

S T R I N G

PSCELUA
(Carries astronauts into space)

C A P S U L E

VIDERR
(Operates the car)

D R I V E R

DGINUDP
(Smooth dessert)

P U D D I N G

UCSICR
(Big top fun)

C I R C U S

ROCTOD
(Helps when you are sick)

D O C T O R

NAPILOMC
(Criticize, find problems with)

C O M P L A I N

Answers

Page 172
Camping

Grill
Cooler
Flashlight
Compass

Tent
Lantern
Sleeping bag

Backpack
Chair
Binoculars

```
E F G G Z V Q L N E I H I X H
P N Y F L U R L L I R G F F
M B I H D O P N S J G S L B R
N P A R W J X U R A J A G Y C
I S B C T Y J O B E S C E F K
C T V H K L V G D H T U S G I
O O S W G P N G L S Y N R C A
R S M T P I A I O M X R A I H
V U K P P C G C G J I E L L C
O U Q E A H F L K Y T L U N C
V Z E K T S I J V S N O C K P
P L A I O T S Y J O E O O I V
S Y Y F T T J U Z O T T C N H D
E Y J R B I W C U Y G O I N X
F S D Y I C Y W P K K A B I Q
```

Page 173
Amazing Phrases

1. a small item displayed on a shelf or in a cabinet

   K NICK - K NACK

2. to travel in a diagonal pattern

   Z IG - Z AG

3. describes someone who can't really make up his mind

   W ISHY - W ASHY

4. to change an opinion completely

   F LIP - F LOP

5. just okay, not great

   SO - SO

6. a ride in which two people take turns going up and down

   S EE - S AW

Page 174
Getting Dressed

ACROSS	DOWN
1 Head	2 Feet
2 Chest	5 Legs
3 Body	
4 Hands	

⁵PANTS
¹HAT
²SHIRTS
³COAT
SHE
⁴GLOVES

Page 175
Decode-a-Message

A=7	G=2	M=5	S=8
C=10	H=12	N=13	T=16
D=3	I=9	O=1	U=4
E=6	L=15	R=11	Y=14

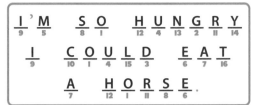

I'M SO HUNGRY
9 5 8 1 12 4 13 2 11 14

I COULD EAT
9 10 1 4 15 3 6 7 16

A HORSE.
7 12 1 11 8 6

Answers

Page 176
Monkey Doubles

Page 177
Valedictorian

VALEDICTORIAN

Here are just a few:

acorn	carnival	divorce	reaction
action	carol	drain	recital
active	carton	drive	retail
actor	carved	editorial	retain
adore	cavern	eviction	rodent
adorn	cedar	ideal	tailor
advance	central	identical	tenor
advent	cider	indicator	tired
advice	civil	invade	toenail
advocate	clarinet	invited	trace
aerial	clean	ironed	trade
airline	clear	ironic	trail
alcove	cleat	later	train
alert	client	learn	trivial
alien	clover	liner	vacant
alive	coated	loaned	vacation
alone	coiled	locate	valiant
alter	coined	loved	vandal
antic	convert	naive	vendor
antler	cover	native	vertical
aorta	crane	noted	video
arena	crate	noticed	violet
article	dancer	ocean	violin
aviation	declaration	older	viral
avoidance	decor	ordeal	vital
calendar	dental	raced	vocal
calorie	detail	radio	voice
canal	diner	radioactive	voter
candle	direction	raincoat	
canoe	diver	rational	
cardinal	divine	ravioli	

Page 178
Outer Space

Page 179
Toys

Answers

Page 180
First Thing First

H
O
M
E
W
O
R
K

Now choose four letters from this word to spell out the capital of a European country.

R O M E

Page 181
Reach for the Beach!

whale

ocean

lotion

pail

fan

pan

Page 182
A Day at the Zoo

Page 183
Duck Pond

Answers

Page 184
Word Scramble

USB
(Kid mover)

<u>B U S</u>

UIST
(Office wear)

<u>S U I T</u>

TGIF
(To give)

<u>G I F T</u>

NSKATIG
(Icy sport)

<u>S K A T I N G</u>

Page 185
Bodies of Water

Pacific   Arctic   Nile
Atlantic   Indian   YuKon
Mediterranean   Caribbean
Red   Mississippi

Page 186
Teatime Mix-Up

A girl and her friend sit down for tea.

A girl pours milk in her friend's cup of tea.

A girl knocks on her friend's door.

5
3
1
6
2
4

Both girls drink their tea!

A girl asks her friend to come over her house.

A girl pours her friend a cup of tea.

Page 187
Sauces

across
1 Eggs
2 Ribs
3 Hot wings

DOWN
4 Pasta
5 Turkey
6 Tortilla Chips

Crossword:
1 HOLLANDAISE
2 BARBECUE
3 RANCH
4 MARINARA
5 GRAVY
6 SALSA

Answers

Page 188
Decode-a-Riddle

W H I C H   C I T Y
U F G A F   A G R W

H A S   N O   P E O P L E
F Y Q   L M   N C M N J C

I N   I T ?
G L   G R

E L E C T R I C I T Y
C J C A R P G A G R W

Page 189
Let's Go Fly a Kite!

Page 190
Unequivocally

UNEQUIVOCALLY

Here are just a few:

acne	cola	lonely	uncle
alcove	cone	love	uncoil
alien	convey	lovely	unequal
alive	cove	loyal	unique
alley	coven	lunacy	vain
alloy	cull	nail	vale
ally	envy	naive	valley
aloe	equal	navel	value
alone	equally	navy	veal
call	evil	nice	veil
cane	icon	nicely	vein
canoe	inlay	noel	vial
cave	lacy	novel	vice
cell	lane	novella	vile
cello	lean	novice	vine
clan	lice	null	vinyl
clay	lilac	ocean	viola
clean	line	oily	vocal
clone	lion	olive	vocally
clove	live	once	voice
cloven	lively	only	yell
clue	loan	ounce	yule
coal	local	oval	
coil	locale	oven	
coin	lone	quail	

Page 191
Snowmobile

Answers

Page 192
Birds of a Feather

Crossword answers:
- 2 Across: PARROT
- 1 Down: TOWN
- 2 Down: PENGUIN
- 4: FLAMINGO
- 5: PEACOCK
- 6: EAGLE

Page 193
Sweet Stuff

 – CUMB – ER +

 – 1 – LOT +

 – T +  – Y

C U P C A K E

Page 194
Word Game

Sneakers are missing laces.

Open book is missing words.

Bumblebee is missing his stripes.

Glasses are missing lenses.

Page 195
First Day of School

Answers

Page 196
Flamingo Frenzy

Page 197
Word Scramble

IVRER
(Body of water)

R I V E R

KAPR
(Place to play)

P A R K

ONOM
(Lights up the night)

M O O N

GSIN
(Speak melodiously)

S I N G

Page 198
What to Do

ARTS AND CRAFTS
BIKE RIDE
BIRD WATCHING
CHARADES
CHECKERS

DANCE
GAME NIGHT
PICNIC
SEE A MOVIE
TOUCH FOOTBALL

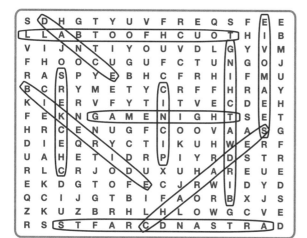

Page 199
Out of Order

1) "I brought a flashlight!" I said.

2) "Run!" I shouted. And we ran out of the cave.

3) I met my best friend at the park.

4) "Why don't we go explore the big cave?" my friend replied.

5) At the cave we stepped into the darkness.

6) And so we headed off to the big cave.

7) I switched on my flashlight.

8) When we were safely back in the park, we laughed and laughed.

9) Suddenly, hundreds of bats came flying toward us.

10) In the park I asked my friend, "What do want to do today?"

<u>3</u> <u>10</u> <u>4</u> <u>6</u> <u>5</u> <u>1</u> <u>7</u> <u>9</u> <u>2</u> <u>8</u>

Answers

Page 200
On the Farm

ACROSS
2 Says "moo!"
3 Farm equipment you drive
4 Keep the animals in.
6 Ready to ride

DOWN
1 Prepare the field
2 How about some eggs?
5 It all starts with these
6 Bales of food

The crossword answers:
- 1 Down: PLOW
- 2 Across: COW / 2 Down: CHICKEN
- 3 Across: TRACTOR
- 4 Across: FENCES / 5 Down: SEEDS
- 6 Across: HORSE / 6 Down: HAY

Page 201
Decode-a-Message

A=3	I=14	S=13
D=10	L=4	T=5
E=16	M=11	U=1
F=17	N=15	W=12
G=2	O=6	Y=7
H=8	R=9	

M O M   A N D   D A D
11 6 11   3 15 10   10 3 10

W E N T   T O   M A U I
12 16 15 5   5 6   11 3 1 14

A N D   A L L   I   G O T
3 15 10   3 4 4   14   2 6 5

W A S   T H I S
12 3 13   5 8 14 13

F U N N Y   T - S H I R T.
17 1 15 15 7   5 13 8 14 9 5

Page 202
Word Game

Secret ← Secret!

TOP SECRET

Page 203
Picnic Basket

PICNIC BASKET

Here are a few:

ask	casket	nick
ate	cast	paste
bank	eat	pet
banks	eats	pets
bat	ice	pick
bean	kin	pin
beans	nab	pins
best	nest	sack
bet	net	tea
cab	nice	test
cabs	nicest	tick

Answers

Page 204
Cornfield

Page 205
In the Garden

Page 206
Birth Watching

AMERICAN GOLDFINCH

Page 207
You are the Poet!

While walking through the FOG,

Out hopped a big, green   FROG .

I stepped away in FRIGHT,

Worried he might   BITE .

Then I remembered THIS,

They don't do that, they   KISS .

Although it made me WINCE.

I made that guy a PRINCE .

Answers

Page 208
Foul Basketball Play

Page 209
Campfire

Page 210
Word Scramble

CRKO
(A stone, pebble, or boulder)

R O C K

LUDBI
(To construct or put together)

B U I L D

TNSE
(Home for birds)

N E S T

DANS
(It's at the beach)

S A N D

RKEBA
(Smash, destroy)

B R E A K

VEERS
(What a waiter does in a restaurant)

S E R V E

GINS
(Belt out a song)

S I N G

ILAS
(Do this on a boat)

S A I L

Page 211
Autumn

Basket	Donut	Foliage
Sweater	Pumpkin	Chocolate
Fireplace	Harvest	
Cider	Apples	

I S W J X V V Z K J E U N D E
I W O K Z U C W O Y F F M R Z
X E J Z T U R S R E F K T W Q
L A F H N K V E C W N E E S F
B T P O N T D G P Q K C G E K
T E T Q J I I Y D S E H A L Z
P R U N C B K F A I O I P P Y
H C N L O I Z B X C R C P A W
A C O F J A K H F I O O L U Y
R B D M Z M Z W U Q E L A F A
V Z N Y L Q Z X C Z P A M P V
E W J N F V J J U C L T U O Z
S A P U M P K I N N A E I P I
T G N W Z F I L D N C J O E I
K F N H Z F D Z E Z E G M J I

283

Answers

Page 212
You Complete the Story!

This is a suggestion (you can create your own story!):

I was walking along the __beach__ when I heard a strange noise. It

sounded like a loud __chicken__ . Looking up, I spotted a huge

__ship__ zooming across the sky. What is that thing, I thought? It looks

like a great big __banana__ . I ran home to tell my __sister__ all

about it. When I got home, much to my shock, the __cow__ I had seen

was sitting in my living room having a cup of __tea__ with my mom

and dad. This was the strangest day I ever had. Except for that time I went to

the __circus__ with a twelve-legged __ape__ !

ROOF · MOUNTAIN · BEACH · ROAD · CHICKEN
APE · COW · BABY · SIREN · SHIP · ROCKET
HOT DOG · BANANA · HEAD · FOOT · SISTER
BROTHER · COUSIN · PET · CHIMP · GOLDFISH · TEA
MILK · COFFEE · BRAINS · CIRCUS · CARNIVAL
PARADE · EGGPLANT · CROCODILE · TEACHER

Page 213
World of Money

across
2 England
5 Israel
7 Twenty-five cents
8 Mexico
9 Ten cents

DOWN
1 Russia
3 United States
4 Five cents
6 Europe
8 One cent

Page 214
Decode-a-Message

A=5	E=7	O=2	R=4
B=6	L=1	P=3	

P	O	L	A	R		B	E	A	R
3	2	1	5	4		6	7	5	4

Page 215
Dinnertime

Answers

Page 216
Fun and Games

Here are a few:

dame	mane	same
dames	mean	sand
fame	men	sang
fan	mend	sea
fang	mug	seam
fangs	nag	send
gem	name	sum
gems	names	sun
gum	sag	sung

Page 217
Winter Maze

Page 218
Body Language

Page 219
Summer Fun

THE BEACH

Answers

Page 220
True or False?

Jupiter is the largest planet in our solar system. __T__

Earth has one moon. __T__

Most of Earth is covered by water. __T__

Astronauts have walked on the moon. __T__

Humans have walked on Mars. __F__

Earth is the third planet out from the sun. __T__

Page 221
Football

Page 222
Bumper Cars

Page 223
Word Scramble

DOLEM
(Likes to pose)

M O D E L

ONGTA
(Dance)

T A N G O

UGLAU
(Happy sound)

L A U G H

PEALP
(Fruit)

A P P L E

CARELL
(Take back)

R E C A L L

NGUYO
(Not old)

Y O U N G

Answers

Page 224
Carnival

People
Popcorn
Rides
Camera
Prizes
Roller coaster
Ferris Wheel
Bumper cars
Cotton candy
Games

Page 225
New Arrangement

H P Y X F D L B S R Q W E O F G

<u>D</u> <u>R</u> <u>O</u> <u>P</u>

Page 226
Let's Dance!

ACROSS
1 ITPOEN — POINTE
2 ELRANILAB — BALLERINA
3 AQEESRABU — ARABESQUE
4 EEELVR — RELEVÉ

DOWN
5 RERAB — BARRE
6 ETEJ — JETE
7 RIPETTEUO — PIROUETTE
8 ILEP — PLIE

¹POINTE

²BALLERINA

³ARABESQUE

⁴RELEVE

⁷PIROUETTE

⁸PLIE

⁵BARRE

⁶JETE

Page 227
Decode-a-Riddle

<u>W H Y</u>   <u>W A S</u>
Y J A   Y C U

<u>T H E</u>   <u>B E L T</u>
V J G   D G N V

<u>A R R E S T E D</u>?
C T T G U V G F

<u>F O R</u>   <u>H O L D I N G</u>
H Q T   J Q N F K P I

<u>U P</u>   <u>T H E</u>   <u>P A N T S</u>
W R   V J G   R C P V U

287

Answers

Page 228
Wonder-Ful

- − + − C + D

+ Y + 1 − E

G R A N D
C A N Y O N

Page 229
Secretary

SECRETARY

Here are just a few:

acres	crater	rates	tease
arrest	create	react	terrace
artery	crest	reset	terse
career	eater	retry	trace
cares	eatery	scare	trays
carry	erase	scary	trees
carts	eraser	stare	years
caterer	racer	starry	yeast
cease	races	steer	
crate	rarest	tears	

Page 230
Clock

Page 231
What Shape Am I?